YOUR SUN SIGN IS YOUR HEALTH SIGN

The Planets and Stars affect every aspect of your physical well being. Now you can learn to recognize and use the energy cycles unique to your Zodiac sign.

- When Your Body Is Most Resistant To Disease

- What Special Vitamin Diet Your Sign Requires

- The Periods When Your Star Sign Becomes Your Sex Sign

- What Illness Affects Your Sign Most

MEDICAL ASTROLOGY

A ZODIAC GUIDE TO PHYSICAL HEALTH

By OMAR V. GARRISON

MEDICAL
ASTROLOGY

MEDICAL ASTROLOGY

How the Stars Influence Your Health

BY OMAR V. GARRISON

WARNER

PAPERBACK LIBRARY
NEW YORK

WARNER PAPERBACK LIBRARY
First Printing: March, 1973

Queries for rights and permissions should be addressed to
University Books, Inc., New Hyde Park, N.Y. 11040.

Library of Congress Catalog Card Number: 79-118602

This Warner Paperback Library Edition is published by arrange-
ment with University Books, Inc.

Cover design and photograph by Henry Wolf

Warner Paperback Library is a division of Warner Books, Inc.,
315 Park Avenue South, New York, N.Y. 10010.

The cosmos is a vast living body, of which we are still parts. The sun is a great heart whose tremors run through our smallest veins. The moon is a great nerve-center from which we quiver forever. Who knows the power that Saturn has over us, or Venus? But it is a vital power, rippling exquisitely through us all the time.

—D. H. Lawrence, *Apocalypse*

Contents

FOREWORD

MEDICAL ASTROLOGY is the art of determining from an individual's horoscope the diseases and infirmities to which he is predisposed.

The stellar patterns at the time of birth are believed to indicate potential illnesses which may be triggered by transits of the planets over sensitive areas of the natal chart during the ensuing years.

There are, of course, a great number of ways the planets can aspect each other. This complexity makes it difficult to establish exact formulas which will pinpoint the presence, either latent or active, of any given disease. For example, there is no simple aspect or sign that, taken alone, can be regarded as a reliable delineation of tuberculosis or cancer. At the same time, there are general arguments or constants in the chart which call for further, detailed analysis.

Accurate judgments require long experience and the ability to view the horoscope as a whole; to balance and correlate the various and often conflicting testimonies before reaching a final conclusion.

For that reason, the reader is cautioned against making a hasty diagnosis based upon a partial reading of his astrological map.

Even when dormant physical disorders are clearly evident in the birth chart, the native may live his whole life without the inherent defects ever becoming active. In fact,

11

one of the chief aims of medical astrology is to *prevent* the occurrence of ill health during those periods in a person's life when his progressed horoscope shows that he will be subject to unusually discordant planetary influences.

It is a well-settled principle in astrology that "the stars incline, they do not compel." So it is important to remember that one's health can always be improved, and planetary afflictions can be largely meliorated or overcome by self-discipline, proper diet, and harmonious thoughts.

Until recently, orthodox medical practice has concerned itself with the diagnosis and treatment of disease only after symptoms appear and the patient consults his doctor because he is already sick. Aside from the check-and-checkup programs sponsored by fund-raising drives for medical research and aimed at limited objectives, comparatively little is being done in the field of predictive medicine.

Important advances have been made in scientific methods for the detection of disease which has already made its presence known; but even the best of these fall far short of infallibility. Testimony before a congressional committee not long ago revealed that laboratory tests such as urinalysis, blood sampling, x-rays, electrocardiograms, etc., usually regarded as highly accurate in identifying ailments, are in fact erroneous 25 percent of the time.

A study made by the Bureau of Laboratories for New York City disclosed an even worse record of laboratory error in America's largest metropolis. Of 425 laboratories investigated, only 100 showed an acceptable degree of accuracy in their work; and 130 were so inefficient that they had to be closed.

A staggering 75 percent of the laboratories surveyed issued inaccurate reports on even simple blood chemistry tests.

While astrology cannot, in the present state of the art, offer the kind of clinical analysis doctors have come to depend upon, it can provide valuable—and sometimes more accurate—clues to the nature and origin of baffling symptoms.

In the area of preventive medical examination, an expertly cast horoscope can be especially helpful.

For example, the medical astrologer, knowing that a prominent and afflicted Jupiter is associated with liver trouble, can determine from other planetary aspects whether and when a disease involving that organ will become manifest. An enzyme test in the laboratory, on the other hand, can diagnose the difficulty only after it has taken hold.

The same is true for all other disease entities. Each has a corresponding planetary formula and birth-chart constant, which alert a healer skilled in astrology, enabling him to make an earlier and sometimes more accurate diagnosis than the physician who relies upon observation of symptoms, laboratory tests, and the patient's medical history.

In the case of terminal diseases, such an early warning system may spell the difference between life and death.

The present work is not a professional textbook of astro-diagnosis, since such a manual, though urgently needed, is beyond the technical competence of the author. Rather, it is meant to serve as an introduction to the subject and to provide the general reader as well as the practicing astrologer with a guide to broad health trends and weaknesses indicated in the horoscope.

For a more detailed analysis and advice on specific problems, the reader should have a specialist in medical astrology (who may also be a physician) erect and interpret his radical and progressed charts.

A growing number of doctors are quietly availing themselves of astrology as a diagnostic aid, even though they still find it professionally unwise to let the fact be known. Some have themselves become proficient in casting horoscopes; others rely upon consultants. I know of one successful and highly regarded doctor in southern California who has enlisted the help of his astrologer-wife in his practice.

Medical science is also beginning to recognize that individuals differ in their needs for biochemical salts, food elements, and vitamins. This is the view long held by astrologers, who have taught that the natives of each sign of the zodiac have certain nutritional requirements and deficiencies which are peculiar to their planetary type.

In the following pages, you will find in the section covering each Sun-sign a list of these essential elements, necessary for the maintenance of good health. Also given is an inventory of foods in which an adequate supply of the nutrient in question may be found.

Proper diet alone, of course, will not insure freedom from illness. It is well known that our emotional lives also play an important role in the development of physical ailments. This being so, I have included for each Sun-sign an analysis of basic personality components, characteristic of that sign. It is just as important to recognize and correct psychological weaknesses as it is to deal with constitutional defects mapped by the birth chart.

Readers familiar with the literature of astrology may be surprised to find in this book yogic breathing techniques appropriate to each zodiacal sign. A moment's reflection, however, will make the connection between astrology and yoga obvious.

As every astrologer knows, the Sun, the giver of life, controls the human vitality and is the most powerful influence in the zodiac—a ball of dazzling radiance which is a million times as large as the earth.

Scientists who have studied the Sun's light by spectro-analysis have reported that all elements known on Earth are represented in solar radiation.

There are four envelopes or luminous layers of emanation around the Sun. The first three are: the *photosphere,* which forms the gaseous crust or surface and from which the brightest light is emitted; the *chromosphere,* a layer of incandescent hydrogen and helium, surrounding the

14

photosphere; and the *corona,* an irregular, shifting radiance with fiery streamers extending many millions of miles into space.

Finally, there is the *zodiacal light,* a nebulous glow which can be seen with the naked eye in the western sky after twilight and in the east just before dawn. In *The Theory of Celestial Influence,* Rodney Collin says of it:

"The zodiacal light evidently represents a lens-shaped cloud of some highly rarefied matter, forming as it were, a second or outer aura of the Sun, which extends in an attenuated form even as far as the orbit of the earth."

According to teachers of yoga in India, it is this "solar breath" or vitally charged particles from the Sun—called *prana*—that is inhaled during the deep-breathing exercises. It is directed to various subtle centers of the body to revitalize them. Oxygen is also taken into the lungs, aiding the body's metabolism; but for the yogis, this is a secondary consideration.

For ready reference, charts and tables giving summarized information concerning cell-salts and dietary supplements, diseases associated with the various planetary aspects, an ephemeris of the Moon, and so on, will be found in the back of the book.

The author takes it for granted that, when symptoms of any illness appear, you will have the good sense to consult a carefully chosen physician regarding your condition, rather than to attempt self-diagnosis and treatment.

15

MEDICAL
ASTROLOGY

THE WISDOM OF 5,000 YEARS

IF YOU'RE a woman in whose horoscope Saturn, Jupiter, and the Moon are all prominent and afflicted, are you inviting cancer if you take the Pill?

Have you a predisposition toward heart trouble if a number of the plants were ill-aspected in the fixed signs (especially Leo and Aquarius) at the moment you were born?

Does the Moon in conjunction with Venus in a birth chart give the native an insatiable desire for pastries and sweets which, if not curbed, will spell overweight in the middle years?

Just a generation ago, to raise such questions as these in intellectual circles would have exposed the person posing them to severe ridicule. He would have been accused of frivolity at best and scientific ignorance at worst.

The academic community was still suffering from a hangover of nineteenth-century scientism—as, indeed, most "-ists" and "-ologists" still are. There was no point, they said, in discussing the absurd notion that there is some kind of correspondence between the movements of the Sun, Moon, and planets and human illnesses or traits of character. According to scientific opinion of the day, the whole system of symbols and "myths" which went by the name of astrology was taken seriously only by the uneducated.

During the past three decades, however, advances made

19

in physics and related disciplines have demolished the materialistic concept of the universe which formerly prevailed.

Not only Einstein's work with gravitational and electromagnetic fields, but recent discoveries made by space scientists and others, support many of the hypotheses of astrology.

Information regarding outer space brought back by our astronauts, for example, has confirmed astrology's claim that the Earth and Sun, the planets and fixed stars, are all charged bodies possessing magnetic fields of differing intensities.

The movements of the Sun and planets cause their angular relationships to each other to change, resulting in a constant variation in the magnetic couplings. An instrument left on the surface of the Moon by Apollo 12's astronauts has provided data showing that the Earth's magnetic field resembles the elongated tail of a comet, owing to the steady flow of gases, impinging upon it from the Sun. Space scientists have reported that this solar wind, as it is called, compresses the magnetic forces on the day side of the Earth (facing the Sun), while the magnetic field on the dark side of the Earth trails our planet in a "wake" several million miles in length.

As the Moon cuts across this magnetic wake, the three-prong sensor left on the Moon radioed back to Earth information concerning the effects of the transit.

Unmanned spacecraft have investigated similar phenomena elsewhere in the solar system, and researchers are still analyzing the data returned to Earth by their instruments. Findings reported to date consistently agree with theories advanced by astrologers in the past.

Experiments currently being carried out in other branches of science are likewise rediscovering some of the ancient truths of astrology. Item: Recent studies conducted by Dr. Robert O. Becker, an orthopedic surgeon at Syracuse Veterans Administration Hospital, have led to the conclusion that astrologers' theories regarding cosmic influences on earthly life may not have been super-stitious nonsense after all.

"He is going back to medicine's dim folklore," reported *Newsweek* magazine, "to try to explain questions that now baffle doctors."

Dr. Becker and his associates found persuasive evidence that there is a direct correlation between admissions to mental hospitals and changes in the magnetic "aura" which surrounds the Earth.

By studying 28,642 admissions to eight large hospitals in the New York area, the researchers found that the number of patients hospitalized for mental illness increased sharply during disturbances in the Earth's magnetic field.

They explained this intriguing correspondence thus: "Subtle changes in the intensity of the geomagnetic field may affect the nervous system by altering the body's own electromagnetic field."

Dr. Becker said that this bioelectric field enveloping the body appears to be generated by the brain and spinal cord.

Although (for obvious reasons) Dr. Becker and his colleagues did not use the word "astrology" in their pub-lished reports, they were, in fact, restating some of the basic hypotheses of astrology. In a paper delivered before a scientific conference at the Massachusetts Institute of Technology, for example, Dr. Becker summed up his work thus:

"We can only suspect a general relationship between the whole human species and the whole electromagnetic phenomena that engage the sun, other stars, and the galaxies."

Medical astrology is prepared to go even further. It seeks to show how these same forces are responsible not only for psychological changes in people, but for con-stitutional weaknesses and predisposition toward various physical ills.

In the past, scientific scoffers at astrology have argued that any form of energy reaching the Earth from the more distant planets of the solar system would be too weak to stimulate a response in the human nervous system.

They reasoned that, if animal organisms did not react to magnetic currents which were infinitely stronger than those reaching them from the planets, they certainly would not be influenced by the comparatively feeble impulses from outer space.

However, recent experiments made by Dr. Frank A. Brown and his associates at Northwestern University have shown that animals placed in extremely weak magnetic fields responded more readily to the diminished levels of energy than to higher intensities.

In fact, earlier research had failed to disclose such a sensitivity precisely because very strong magnetic fields were used in the experiments. The more powerful magnetic force had overwhelmed the biological organism, so to speak, preventing *any* reaction.

Another significant discovery made by the Brown research team was that living organisms enclosed for prolonged periods in hermetically sealed compartments still responded to subtle, extraterrestrial influences which penetrated their scientifically devised isolation.

There is also growing experimental evidence that our blood is directly influenced by the Sun and Moon, and possibly by other celestial bodies. Dr. Maki Takata of Toho University in Tokyo found that the composition of human blood varies in reaction to solar eruptions, eclipses, and changes occurring at sunrise.

Several years ago, a Florida doctor compiled data which established a statistical correlation between the flow of blood in our bodies and the changing phases of the Moon. Dr. Edson J. Andrews, an eye, ear, nose, and throat specialist had observed that, at certain times, all his patients recovered from surgery without experiencing dangerous hemorrhaging. At other times, just the opposite occurred: The majority experienced serious bleeding that required emergency treatment.

Dr. Andrews's nurse (who may or may not have had

22

some knowledge of astrology) suggested that the bleeding episodes might be related to the lunar cycle. Dr. Andrews reacted to that theory with one word: "Nonsense."

However, the nurse circled dates on the office calendar when postoperative crises occurred. They were all clustered around the date of the full Moon.

During the next three years, Dr. Andrews kept careful records on more than 1,000 tonsillectomy cases. He found that 82 percent of the bleeding crises requiring emergency treatment occurred between the Moon's first and third quarters.

To double-check these data, he persuaded one of his medical colleagues to undertake similar research. Results of the two studies were almost identical.

Although science had no immediate explanation for the phenomenon, the Moon obviously exerted a decisive influence on Man's "internal sea."

That's what astrological tradition had been studying since the time of Ptolemy. Few scientists, however, have cared (or dared) to make an impartial and unbiased investigation of the claim.

Dismissing the accumulated wisdom of 5,000 years as pseudo-science and "fantasy of the skies," they have asserted that astrologers' lack of academic background and objectivity makes their research unacceptable to orthodox science.

At the same time, they have excused their refusal to examine the available evidence, with the condescending explanation that "science has more pressing tasks."

"Life is short and there is a lot to do," Professor Gibson Reaves, University of Southern California astronomer, was quoted as saying not long ago. "I can either work on something I know will be useful or on astrology."

Just how useful to our society, or to mankind as a whole, some of astronomy's far-out research has been is a matter of wildely divergent opinion.

Unlike most of his fellow astronomers, who vehemently declare that astrology is nothing more than superstition under a thin coat of mathematics, however, Professor Reaves admits that science has no scientific proof to support such an indictment.

"Some people say they don't see how astrology could work," he told the *New York Times,* "but nobody has ever *proved* finally that it doesn't."

Although astronomy is the lineal descendant of astrology, Reaves, for some reason, felt that it was the sociologist who should undertake the job of demonstrating once and for all whether astrology does or does not work.

"It's the social scientists, I think, who are missing a bet by not looking into its influence," Professor Reaves declared.

It is noteworthy that, while censuring astrologers for their alleged shortcoming in scholarship, the doctrine scientists have, in the past, led the fight to prevent astrologers from establishing a legal board of examiners to pass on the academic qualifications of their practitioners, in the same way that similar state and county boards certify physicians, chiropractors, and even barbers.

An outstanding instance of this ambivalence occurred several years ago in California. Astrologers there tried to have a bill introduced in the state legislature, setting up a Board of Astrological Examiners. The act provided that only persons over 25 years of age who had studied astrology for five years or more, and who could meet certain standards of ethics and proficiency, would be licensed as practitioners.

Scientific circles in the state, headed by astronomers, mounted such vigorous opposition to the measure that it was killed in committee.

NEW CLIMATE OF INQUIRY

It is only fair to add that, while most of the high priests of science still regard astrology as an outrageous caricature of scientific determinism, this attitude is slowly changing.

24

A new climate of unbiased inquiry seems increasingly to prevail among younger scholars.

At Stanford University's counseling and testing center, for example, Dr. Ralph Metzner follows the example of the late pioneer in psychiatry, Dr. Carl G. Jung, and uses astrology in his professional work as a psychologist. *Time* magazine has quoted him as predicting that astrology will soon become an accepted adjunct to psychology and psychiatry, because a properly erected natal chart "is much more complex and sophisticated than present psychological maps or systems."

Dr. Jung made the same prediction. "Astrology is assured of recognition from psychology without further restrictions," he said, "because astrology represents the summation of all psychological knowledge of antiquity."

Dr. Jung called the ancient wisdom *scientia intuitiva,* whose postulates are based on centuries of experience, recorded in the collective unconscious.

"As we all know," he wrote in *Psychology and Alchemy,* "science began with the stars, and mankind discovered in them the dominants of the unconscious, the 'gods' as well as the curious psychological qualities of the zodiac: a complete, projected theory of human character."

Jung put forward a theory he called *synchronicity* to account for the correspondence between the movement of celestial bodies and events on Earth.

Simply stated, synchronicity means that whatever happens anywhere in the universe is stamped with the character of the moment at which it happens. "Whatever is born or done this moment of time, has the qualities of this moment of time."

This principle, if taken at face value, would eliminate any cause-and-effect relationship between the stars and mundane events. Emanations from the planets would not cause a person born at a certain time to have certain characteristics or constitutional weaknesses. Instead, the two events—birth and planetary pattern in the heavens—are merely coincidental. It amounts to nothing more than arbitrarily relating two items of experience or reality because they occurred simultaneously.

If Jung's basic premise is valid, one might just as well erect a natal chart based on the reading of clocks in motion in the world's various time zones, or one's gas meter at the time of birth. We should no longer have astrology in the traditional meaning of the term, but something else—a theory of qualitative time called synchronicity.

It is difficult to see how the theory of synchronicity provides a more satisfactory explanation of why astrology works than did earlier theories based upon the assumption of astral influences.

It certainly could not account for the phenomena reported by researchers such as those discussed in foregoing paragraphs—Drs. Becker, Brown, and Andrews.

Furthermore, I suspect that, if pursued far enough, the concept would lead us into strange paradoxes and untenable conclusions. There is something far more mysterious, far more direct than just "meaningful coincidence" involved in man's relationship with the universe.

As a matter of fact, after hearing Dr. Max Knoll read a scientific paper on solar proton radiation, Jung himself had second thoughts concerning synchronicity as an explanation of astrological correspondence (a fact that apparently has gone unnoticed by many astrologers who yearn for prestigious approval of their art).

In a lecture which he delivered at the Eranos meeting in Ascona, Switzerland in 1951, Dr. Jung said:

"In the light of the most recent astrophysical research, astrological correspondence is probably not a matter of synchronicity but, very largely, of a causal relationship. As Professor Knoll has demonstrated at this meeting, the solar proton radiation is influenced to such a degree by planetary conjunctions, oppositions and quartile aspects that the appearance of magnetic storms can be predicted with a fair amount of probability. Relationships can be established between the curve of the earth's magnetic disturbances and the mortality rate that confirm the unfavorable influence of conjunctions, oppositions, and quartile aspects and the favorable influence of trine and sextile aspects.

"So it is probably a question here of a causal relationship, i.e., of a natural law that excludes synchronicity or restricts it."

Later in the same paper, he made this important observation: "Although the psychological interpretation of horoscopes is still a very uncertain matter, there is nevertheless some prospect today of a causal explanation in conformity with natural law. Consequently, we are no longer justified in describing astrology as a mantic method, that is, fortune-telling. Astrology is in the process of becoming a science."

Admittedly, a wide gap still exists between all of astrology's ancient theories and science's current conclusions; but the hiatus grows narrower each year.

THE WEDDING OF ASTROLOGY AND MEDICINE

There is no general agreement among scholars as to exactly when the marriage between astrology and medicine took place. We find the two scientific arts intimately associated from the remotest period of prehistory.

Occultists start with the legend of Atlantis. They maintain that the priest-physicians of that lost continent treated all illnesses as basically a discord between man's physical body and extraterrestrial influences.

Most historians, however, hold that astrological medicine originated with the ancient Chaldeans, who were the first to make a systematic study of the stars and planets, and to keep exact records of their movements.

These early Mesopotamian scholars also began to observe a correlation between the configurations of celestial bodies and the appearance of various diseases, both in the individual and as national epidemics.

Each planet was also identified with certain herbs, which were gathered at specific times and used for medicines to treat diseases associated with the planets ruled by them.

There seems little doubt that the motion of a correspondence between planetary aspects and disease was first suggested by the obvious influence of the Sun on all forms of life.

The peoples of antiquity were aware that growth and maturity of plant life and, to a large extent, of man, depended upon the great luminary which governed by day.

"The sun is the light and life of all things created," declared a venerable Hindu text; and the *Gayatri,* India's oldest prayer, repeated each dawn by devout Hindus to this day, is a salutation to the Sun (or rather, to the ineffable Being whose vehicle it is).

The Egyptians also regarded the Sun as both a physical and a titular deity (adored as Ra and Amun-ra) "the real sun, the ruler of the firmament, and the ideal ruler of the universe as king of the gods."

Phoenicians, Persians, Israelites—all acknowledged the powerful influence of the supreme light upon whose rising all other lights disappear.

Likewise the Moon, "when she walked in her brightness" like the ghost of the Sun, was known to control the tides and to affect the germination of seeds.

It is interesting to note that recent experiments with Moon rocks brought back to Earth by astronauts Neil Armstrong and Edwin Aldrin, Jr., have provided laboratory proof that the Moon does affect plant life, just as the ancients claimed.

Dr. Charles H. Walkinshaw, a botanist at NASA's Manned Spacecraft Center in Houston, Texas, discovered that plants exposed to moondust outgrew others which were not treated with the lunar material.

He said the purpose of the experiments had been to determine whether the moondust would be harmful to Earth plants.

"We started with some very primitive plants—liverwort and fern. We put a bit of powdered rock from the Sea of Tranquility on some of them and left others in their natural state. First thing you know, the moondust plants were very clearly ahead of others in growth."

The Moon-treated plants eventually grew four times as large as those of the same class that were not stimulated with lunar dust.

The NASA researchers also reported that moondust made tobacco plant tissue greener and lettuce seeds grow faster than normally.

"We don't know how it works," Dr. Walkinshaw admitted. "It's not a fertilizer, but you'd have to call it some kind of growth promoter."

INTERPRETERS OF THE GODS

Despite what many modern opponents of astrology say, not all civilized peoples of antiquity regarded the Sun, Moon, and planets as gods in themselves—that is, as heavenly beings who acted independently of natural law to influence men's destinies on Earth.

Even though they identified each plant with the *power* of a given deity, some of the earliest astrologers called them *Interpreters,* which made known to man the will of the gods whose names they bore.

The German scholar, Troels-Lund, says that the Chaldeans who wrote a history of creation on seven clay tablets, which have come down to us, regarded the Sun and Moon as "lights kindled by a mighty God, and intended to move day and night in an established order under the dome of heaven.

"But the other five planets! It was unnecessary to be a Chaldean on the Babylonian Tower in order to feel amazement at these. Everyone who had ever followed with his eye their courses for a few nights during a caravan journey; everyone who, lying awake, had occasionally tried to read the time from the only clock of the night—the star-covered canopy of heaven—was bound to have noticed their peculiarities as to light and course.

"They did not shine uniformly, but sometimes intensely, at other times faintly; and entirely different was their radiance from that of other stars—reddish, greenish, bluish. Also, their courses were at one time rapid, at other times slow; then backward or oblique. Sometimes they disappeared entirely.

"Necessarily, they appeared inexplicable not only to the inexperienced observer, but to a still higher grade of intellect, that of the most well-informed Chaldean. For, although their periods could possibly be calculated, their courses beggared all geometrical figures. These confused paths could be explained only in one way—namely, as the expression of an arbitrary will."

Among the Konyunjik collection of cuneiform tablets in the British Museum, dating from the time of the Assyrian king Asshurbanapal (669–628 B.C.), are a number which deal with medical astrology. From these we learn something of the art of astro-diagnosis as it was practiced in those remote times:

"If Mercury rises on the fifteenth day of the month, there will be many deaths." (Tablet 163)

"If an eclipse occurs during the morning watch, and lasts throughout the watch, while the wind blows from the north, those who are ill in Akkad will recover." (Tablet 271)

"If Venus approaches the constellation of Cancer, pregnant women will carry their confinements to a favorable delivery." (Tablet 207)

Some of the inscriptions concern veterinary medicine, a subject of considerable interest to an agricultural people who owned livestock.

In Egypt, even before the First Dynasty, astrology, medicine, and religion were all taught as one body of knowledge. Egyptian practitioners, who were the most accomplished physicians in the ancient world, used astrology to diagnose their patients' illnesses. They then prescribed herbal remedies or, where necessary, surgery, according to a projection of the heavens.

The astrologer-healers had at their disposal a vast array of medicinal herbs, roots, barks, and decoctions, all of them classified according to their sidereal as well as their therapeutic properties. The ancient Greek poet Homer remarks on "the infinity of drugs produced in Egypt"; and Pliny often alludes to the same thing.

Knowledge concerning some of the more exotic of these preparations was closely guarded, being divulged only to initiate priests. Over the intervening centuries, the greater part of this esoteric tradition has been lost to us. Stories such as the strange account of the *Amanita muscaria* in Dr. Andrija Puharich's unusual book, *The Sacred Mushroom,* suggest that modern pharmacologists might have something to learn from the buried archives of Egypt.

From Mesopotamia and Egypt, the "Chaldean science" —including medical astrology—spread throughout the known world of the time. It reached its fullest and final development in the Hellenistic culture, when Greek genius expanded and refined it into a precise system that has come down to us almost unchanged.

The use of planetary data in the practice of the healing arts won wide acceptance among the most eminent physicians of the classical world.

Hippocrates (460–377 B.C.), known as the father of medicine, not only made a profound study of astrology himself, but urged his students to do likewise, declaring that "the man who is ignorant of astrology is to be regarded as fool rather than physician." He was the first physician to use astrological data to determine crises in the course of diseases.

In the *Corpus Hippocraticum,* the principal work of early Greek medicine, is the following passage:

"Attention must be paid to the rise of the stars, and especially that of Sirius, as well as to the rise of Arcturus;

31

and further, to the setting of the Pleiades, for most diseases reach a crisis during those periods."

Elsewhere in the same work, physicians are reminded that astrology "is not of slight, but of very essential importance in the medical art."

More than two millennia after Hippocrates, Louis Mac-Neice quoted an American physician who heartily agreed with the father of his profession: "The doctor needs astro-diagnosis worse than he can ever realize until he has used it for some years."

THE ALEXANDRIAN SCHOOLS

After his conquest of Egypt and Chaldea, Alexander the Great established a medical school and museum in Alexandria, then one of the chief centers of learning in the ancient world. For more than three centuries thereafter, scholars from all parts of the Mediterranean journeyed to the Egyptian city to complete their studies in medicine.

One of the graduate students who enrolled at the center was Galen, a native of Pergamum in Asia Minor, who was to remain the dominant figure in medicine for more than a thousand years.

There is no historical record indicating that Galen had any personal contact with his famous contemporary, Claudius Ptolemy, "the prince of astrologers," who lived and taught in Alexandria at that time. However, it seems more than likely that Ptolemy would have lectured on medical astrology at the Alexandrian school, since he was a leading authority on the subject. (Ptolemy's *Tetrabiblos*, a definitive work of astrology still referred to in our time, first appeared in 140 A.D.)

Galen, like his illustrious predecessor Hippocrates, regarded a study of celestial phenomena in its relation to disease as an important part of the healing art. In his well-known treatise, *De Metodo Medendi*, he notes that "the state of the sky, season of the year and region or

32

country" should all be considered in diagnosing and treating human ills.

Drawing from the traditions of Assyria, Babylonia, and Egypt, Galen also wrote a work entitled *Prognostication of Disease by Astrology,* a system of foretelling the course and termination of a disease by employing astronomical data.

In Imperial Rome, where astrology flourished—first among the upper classes, then among the general populace —Galen established what in our time would be called a fashionable practice among the Patricians. In second-century Rome, for a physician to achieve such prominence was unusual indeed. As a profession, medicine was regarded as beneath the consideration of all Roman citizens of any education or social standing.

In odd contrast to their pioneering work in public health (they provided sanitation and safe water supply for their cities as early as the sixth century B.C.), Romans left the physical well-being of the individual largely in the hands of Greek doctors, whom they regarded with open contempt.

Pliny the Elder (23–79 A.D.) expressed the prevailing attitude of his countrymen when he complained that there was no law in the Roman code that provided capital punishment for physicians. "They learn by our suffering," he wrote, "and they experiment by putting us to death."

But while Romans entertained a strong dislike of Greek doctors and Greek medicine as such, they gradually began to accept the Hellenistic system of astrology, including *Medicina Astrologica.*

THE ZODIACAL MAN

The earliest-known Latin treatise on astrology, the *Astronomicon* of the Roman scholar Manilius, written during the reign of Augustus Caesar (31 B.C.–14 A.D.), introduced the concept of zodiacal man. According to this system, each organ and anatomical part of the human body was put under the dominant influence of one of the signs of the zodiac. Thus, the head was said to be ruled by Aries, the neck by Taurus, and so on.

Horoscopes cast for prominent persons, including Roman emperors, gave detailed and sometimes ruthlessly frank appraisals of the native's future health and personal habits.

The horoscope of Emperor Hadrian's father, for example, noted that he would become "disinclined towards natural intercourse, and inflamed about the genitals."

After the collapse of the Roman Empire, the knowledge and practice of astrology declined, along with learning in other fields. We owe its revival several centuries later to the Arabs, aided by the work of Jewish scholars of the Alexandrian school.

Despite the fact that many authoritative Talmudists regarded astrology as contrary to the Law of Israel (because it had been taught to men by the rebellious angels), many Hebrew men of learning became adept in the practice of it.

Abraham, "the exalted father" of the ancient Hebrew people, was himself a Chaldean, born in the Moon-worshipping city of Ur. According to Jewish scriptural narratives, Abraham wore upon his breast an engraved astrological tablet on which every man could decipher his future. The haggadistic writers report that all the kings of East and West gathered every morning at the great patriarch's door to ask his counsel.

It was the Jews, in fact, who in their secret traditions apparently preserved the knowledge of astrology, dating from the Babylonian and Egyptian period of their history. Certainly, during the Middle Ages, they emerged as leading exponents of the art. The *Jewish Encyclopedia* states:

"In the eighth and ninth centuries, Jews were the foremost masters in astrology. Jacob ibn Tarik, called by Ibn Ezra an astrological authority, is recorded by the same writer as having imported the astronomical tables of the Hindus to Baghdad under Almansur in 777."

It was also in the eighth century that the celebrated Caliph of Baghdad, Harun-al-Raschid, ordered the translation into Arabic of Ptolemy's famous text, the *Almagest*. When the Moors overran and conquered Spain, they took with them this and other works on celestial influences, some of them heavily tinged with Jewish mysticism.

It was in this way that astrology was reintroduced into medieval Europe. Departments of astrology were established in the universities of Cordova and Toledo, to which students from all over the continent came to learn the science of the stars.

Astro-medicine formed an important part of the literature of this period, including diagnosis by planetary aspects, the preparation and use of herbal remedies according to their sidereal correspondence, critical days in the course of illnesses, and general rules for preserving one's health.

Peter of Spain (1210–1277 A.D.), the noted scholar who became Pope John XXI, was a practicing astrologer, who left several treatises on the relationship of man's physical well-being to the state of the heavens. In his *History of Magic and Experimental Science,* Thorndike quotes one of these works, in which Peter asserts that the movement of the superior bodies is one of the causes of the shortening of human life. The following passage will give some idea of his style, which is more reminiscent of Rabelais than of a future Pontiff:

"Let the Jews blush, the Saracens be put to confusion, roving practitioners desist, old enchantresses be dumb, and empirics and methodics keep silence. Let rational physicians rejoice and those descendants of the medical art who employ both reason and experience. I, master Petrus Hispanus, a native of Compostela, have pursued by education in all Italy, Burgundy, Vienne, Provence, Gascony, and certain parts of Spain. Certain useful natural phenomena which are not found in the bosom of the art of medicine, I have discovered by labor, vision, chance, experience and genius to be both useful against diseases and the cause of diseases."

The resurgence of astrology which occurred throughout Europe in the thirteenth century grew until it held sway over all the learned professions and classes. It was accepted by the best minds and most eminent thinkers of the period. Chairs of astrology were established in all the important universities, including those at Paris, Bologna, Salamanca, Padua, Rome, Florence, and Vienna. A recent German writer calls the age "one of the most wonderful pages in the history of the development of our race, for an actual *furor astrologicus* seized upon the world. . . ."

Not only scholars, but kings, popes, and noblemen became adepts in the art. For example, Charles V, the German emperor, was tutored in astrology by the future Pope Hadrian VI. The famous astronomer, Tycho Brahe, taught the casting of nativities at the royal court of Denmark.

When Catherine di Medici came to France as the wife of Henry II, she brought a retinue of prominent astrologers from Florence. It is said that she herself was accomplished at erecting judicial charts and rarely embarked upon any important undertaking without consulting them.

Astrological medicine also played an important role in the lives of those at court. Catherine retained the services of Michel de Notredame, a physician-astrologer who had excited favorable comment and wide discussion because of his success in treating victims of plague in 1546. He was a Jewish convert to Christianity, who was later to become famous for his prophecies under the Latin form of his name—Nostradamus.

The physicians and surgeons of that day left voluminous writings on the subject of astro-medicine. These works comprise not only an invaluable compendium of traditional knowledge prior to that age, but also contain much information about the healing properties of many herbs.

It is only because of the blind bias of orthodox scholarship that this body of literature is not available to the modern student. The manuscripts and books remain locked away in the library archives of European universities and museums.

THE CONSILIA OR CASE HISTORIES

In addition to professional treatises to aid their colleagues in the practice of medicine, doctors of the fourteenth and fifteenth centuries also published *Consilia* or case histories of their more interesting or more prominent patients.

In those days when libel laws did not exist, the writers not only discussed in the most intimate detail the nature and symptoms of their patients' complaints, but usually added a general analysis of their characters and mode of living.

Thorndike mentions one such book, printed in Venice in 1552, which dealt with the case histories of 7 popes, 29 cardinals and prelates, 34 secular rulers, 41 men of letters and learning, and 9 persons of imperfect or mutilated physique.

Thorndike observes that, while the professed aim of the work is to lay an experimental foundation for the art of casting nativities, "it is probable that the sale of the volume was increased by the inclusion of so many well-known names and persons in high places."

One has only to imagine what the sale today would be of a prominent doctor's private case book dealing candidly with eminent political and professional people, to understand why, even in sixteenth-century Italy, the *Tractus* would become a best-seller.

By the late eighteenth century, the use of astrology in the diagnosis and treatment of disease had disappeared from the practice of orthodox medicine—at least publicly. Then, as now, a number of doctors continued privately to use astrological charts to help them determine what has been called the common denominator of disease—the relationship the patient has with his own present, past, and possibly future illnesses. In other words, they very sensibly realized that a single ailment is often part of an underlying constant in the individual's integral nature.

They understood that it was necessary to treat not just an ulcer or heart disease (or even some contagious diseases such as tuberculosis and typhoid), but the whole man.

This idea appears to be enjoying a renascence in the practice of modern medicine. In an address before the New York Academy of Medicine, George Draper, M.D., formerly associate professor of clinical medicine at Columbia University, noted that prior to Pasteur's discoveries, which provided a firm basis for the germ theory of disease, doctors thought more about the *nature* of the sick man.

"Modern specialism," he said, "has succeeded well in taking Humpty Dumpty apart, but as yet there is no clear formula which enables us to understand the unique individual as a vibrant, living whole."

It probably never occurred to Dr. Draper that his predecessors of centuries past had solved the problem of comprehending the patient as a unique, living entity by consulting an accurate horoscope. If such an idea did occur to him, it is more than likely that he dismissed the practice as medieval superstition.

But, if your physician will not examine your horoscope before he treats you, perhaps you can at least examine *his*. Finding out when and where he was born may not be easy, unless he condescends to "go along" with your harmless irrationality.

From an astrological point of view, erecting such a chart for your doctor is well worth the trouble. Acknowledged experts in astro-medicine have said that, if there is not stellar harmony between healer and patient, a cure may be retarded or—in extreme cases—blocked altogether.

The late Howard L. Cornell, M.D., who employed astrology in his long practice and became an authority on the subject, said that the first and most important rule to be observed in comparing the horoscopes of doctor and

38

patient was to make certain that the rising signs in both charts are in harmony. In other words, the two ascendants should belong to the same triplicity (fire, earth, or air) and should be in sextile or trine aspects to each other.

For example, "if the patient has Aries on the ascendant at birth, his healer, for best success, should also have a fiery sign on the ascendant—as Leo or Sagittarius. If the healer employed in this case should have Cancer, Libra or Capricorn upon the ascendant at birth, he would tend to affect the patient adversely, or cause him to get worse."

Max Heindel, Rosicrucian authority on astrology, has observed that, in any case, if the healer's Saturn is on the ascendant or in the Sixth House of the patient, the prospects for a cure are not good.

If you suspect that your condition is worsening because you are being treated by an inharmonious physician, Dr. Cornell suggests a change of doctors. He believes that the sextile or trine aspect between the rising signs of doctor and patient will tend naturally to inspire mutual faith and confidence, whereas the square or opposition aspects between them may result in mutual aversion, similar to that which occurs between two persons who marry when their natal horoscopes are inharmonious.

Is it really important to go to such lengths in choosing one's doctor?

Perhaps a partial answer to that question may be found in some startling revelations made in a recent book, *The Doctors,* by sociologist Martin L. Gross.

Citing a survey of iatrogenic (doctor-caused) illness and deaths, made by the chief resident at the Yale-New Haven Hospital and published in the *Annals of Internal Medicine,* Gross concludes that "it might be conservative to estimate death from doctor-caused disease in the magnitude of 200,000 a year."

The writer then adds the grim corollary that "physicians and modern medicine have thus become a close rival of cancer and heart disease as a major killer of man."

In the light of such hair-raising disclosures, perhaps the

insights to be found in a carefully erected horoscope of one's doctor might not be so much a return to the Dark Ages as a projection into a future era of enlightenment.

HEALTH AND THE SUN SIGNS

♈ ARIES
The Ram

(March 21 through April 19)

Planetary Ruler: Mars (♂)
Related to: Head, face, brain, upper jaw, eyes.
Your Body Needs: Foods containing potassium phosphate.
You Should Develop: Patience and moderation.
You Should Avoid: Dissipation of life force; obstinacy and alcohol.

The Sun's entry into the sign of Aries marks the vernal equinox (when night and day are of equal length), the beginning of the zodiacal year.

If you were born in the northern hemisphere during this period, you crossed the threshold of the unseen into earthly life at a time when all nature was eager and riotous with its active principle. Millions of green shoots were pushing through the moist ground, and buds were opening to the light. It was a magical time of blossoms and bird song. Perhaps that is why the ancient Chinese believed that the constellation of Aries had reached the center of the heavens at the time of the world's creation.

As the vital breath of life entered your body for the first time, you inhaled, as it were, an urge to creative action that has remained with you ever since.

Dr. W. J. Tucker describes that critical moment as one "in which the lines of force of the resultant magnetic field

43

of sun, moon and stars—running through the child's body —fix and determine the relative positions of the electrons and protons in the atoms of the child's flesh, blood and bones for the duration of its life."

Despite the dynamism and boldness of your character, the source of your seemingly boundless energy is not, in fact, limitless. There is the ever-present tendency on your part to overestimate it and in consequence to overtax your physical strength. Because the most active part of your body is your brain, you have an overweening confidence that the rest of your physique can match its vitality in carrying out the many plans and pursuits with which the typical Arien is constantly involved.

This is rarely the case. As a result, your intense enthusiasm and your ambition for leadership and trail blazing, sometimes lead you to make unreasonable demands on your reserve of energy.

You are fortunate in that, if not ill-aspected, the Sun in Aries endows the native with the resistance to throw off disease when it attacks. Very few hopeless invalids are found among Ariens; the will power to overcome illness and the burning desire to "get back into action" is too strong to allow a prolonged siege of ill health.

At the same time, this contempt for infirmity has its negative side. It can sometimes cause you to return to your heavy work load when you should remain in bed. You would do well to let your physician, your life partner, or a knowledgeable friend be the judge of your fitness to take up where you left off when illness struck.

Specific dangers to your health will be indicated in the planetary aspects of your individual birth chart. Generally speaking, however, all natives of your sign should guard against head colds and eyestrain; and should have frequent dental checkups. Avoid quarrels or mental upsets, often brought on by your quick temper and resentment of any criticism, whether it is justified or not.

Traditional astrology over the centuries has come to associate certain diseases with each sign of the zodiac.

Ariens are reportedly susceptible to strokes, fevers, skin eruptions, impaired memory, neuralgia of the head and face, vertigo, and nervous exhaustion. Many, if not all, of these complaints can be prevented by careful attention to daily habits, self-discipline, and a well-balanced diet.

With advancing years, you must find interests that will keep you busy or you will tend to become despondent. Since Aries is a mental sign, there are many pleasant activities, such as reading, club affairs, or participation in one of the creative arts, which can occupy your time without requiring you to expend all your reserve of physical vitality.

Another important piece of advice: Ariens are often accident prone (especially if their Sun is severely afflicted or Saturn and Uranus are prominent in the birth chart); so you should exercise great care in handling sharp tools or instruments, and in driving an automobile.

A thirty-year study of astrological correspondences, made by the Brotherhood of Light in Los Angeles, disclosed that a progressed aspect to Mars (your planetary ruler) was present in 100 percent of the charts analyzed for accidents of all kinds, including automobile mishaps.

YOUR PERSONALITY PROFILE

Some of the key words most often used by experienced astrologers to describe Aries people are: venturesome, courageous, headstrong, candid, optimistic, opinionated, brilliant, changeable, high-strung, enterprising, brusque, idealistic, generous, and sometimes foolhardy.

That all adds up to quite an impressive profile. But there is more. Your eagerness to champion the cause of the underdog or the destitute sometimes leads you into wasting your time, effort, and money on the unworthy.

You are happiest and accomplish most when you are your own boss, doing things your own way. Nothing is more frustrating or more injurious to your emotional

45

stability than to be placed in a job where you have to take orders from an executive whom you regard as your inferior (and that goes for a large percentage of all executives).

Although you are an avid reader, interested in a wide range of subjects, your pursuit of knowledge often lacks direction or purpose, and you end up with a confused hodgepodge of information.

A cherished Arien friend of mine, recently deceased, possessed this characteristic to a marked degree. He bore a striking resemblance—both in physical appearance and mannerisms—to the cartoon character Mr. Magoo. In fact, I have reason to believe that he inspired creation of that renowned personage.

I can still hear his powerful, booming voice, holding forth upon a bewildering series of topics which reflected his latest forays into literature, science, and philosophy. From time to time, he would pause in his astonishing monologue to ask:

"Do you get my thought?"

And, of course, one nodded in a half-dazed way, even though one did not have the foggiest notion of what he was talking about.

As an Aries person, you need to stop from time to time to ask yourself: Exactly where am I going? Am I deceiving myself or being deceived by circumstances or by others whom I've endowed with qualities and virtues they don't possess? Am I undermining my health by pushing too hard?

Laurel Lowell, writing in the *Moon Sign Book,* had this sobering and accurate comment to make concerning those born under the influence of Aries: "Ariens generally manage to make generous contributions to their own demise."

With your excellent mental endowment and strong constitution, you can prove this writer wrong, if you will just take the time to think seriously about it.

YOUR GUIDE TO DIET

The ram is indifferent to or indiscriminate in what he eats, unless there are counter-indications in his horoscope.

Not that you do not enjoy good food and drink, especially when it is shared with companions harmonious to your sign—Gemini, Leo, Sagittarius, or Aquarius. If you are a host, you will lay a splendid table, often serving exotic foods and fine wines. But when you dine alone (which you dislike), or *en famille,* you are more likely to be preoccupied with matters other than cuisine.

During the latter decades of your life, it would be advisable to eat less than during the period of peak activity. You should avoid a diet too heavy in fats, which many medical researchers now believe to be a factor in the development of arteriosclerosis (hardening of the arteries). Ariens have a predisposition toward strokes, which are caused by the narrowing and eventual blockage of small blood vessels in the head.

You should also try to stop smoking, if you are addicted to the habit, since tobacco is a vaso-constrictor—that is, it causes a temporary narrowing of the blood vessels.

Although digestive troubles are not common to your sign, provided your Moon and Venus are not ill-aspected, there is more than an even chance that your body will be deficient in the cell-salt potassium phosphate, also called Kali Phosphoricum.

Potassium phosphate is needed by Ariens because it helps to rebuild brain cells and nerve tissue and to restore some of the mental vigor so prodigally expended by those of your sign.

A depletion of this nutrient will result in irritability, headaches, nervous dyspepsia, and a general feeling of exhaustion.

Fortunately, potassium phosphate is found in many

ordinary foods. These include beets, celery, lettuce, cauliflower, watercress, spinach, onion, mustard, radish, carrots, cucumbers, dates, apples, walnuts, and lemons.

Your diet should also include an adequate amount of organic iron and muscle-building proteins, found in lean meat and legumes.

Some of the more common herbs associated with your sun sign are: aloes, basil, bayberry, capsicum, capers, Oregon grape, red pepper, peppermint, and horseradish.

YOGIC BREATHING EXERCISE FOR ARIES

While proper diet will go a long way toward maintaining a balance in bodily functions, another important factor necessary for good health is the vitality taken into the body with the breath, called *prana* by the Hindus.

According to the Indian tests, *prana* is the total energy, manifest and unmanifest, in the cosmos. On our planet, it reaches us as the seven-rayed emanation from the Sun. It vitalizes the millions of cells which make up our physical bodies, charging them with an *elan vital.*

Thus, the breathing exercises practiced by yogis are not aimed merely at increasing the oxygen content of the blood, as in the case of deep-breathing exercises performed in Western gymnasiums. Rather, their objective, as explained earlier in this book, is the absorption and distribution throughout the body of the energizing Sun breath.

For each zodiacal sign, there is a breathing exercise which, if performed daily at the proper time, will enable a person born during that period to draw into his lungs the maximum amount of the universal solar energy.

Here is the exercise recommended for Aries:

Time: Between the hours of 9 and 11 A.M.
Place: Outdoors in full sunlight; or in a well-ventilated room where the air is fresh and pure. Try to avoid drafts.
Duration of practice: 5 minutes.

Technique: Sit or stand erect, so that your shoulders are thrown back and your spine is straight. For a moment, try to relax mentally, to "let go," expelling from your mind and consciousness all the worldly concerns that have built up tensions inside you.

Now, inhale slowly, counting as you do so, up to seven. Pause for one count. Then exhale, again slowly, counting to seven. Repeat this breath cycle eight times.

The second phase of the exercise is performed by first pursing the lips, as though about to whistle. Then thrust the tongue forward between the teeth until it touches the lips. Closing both nostrils with the thumb and forefinger of the right hand, inhale through the narrow opening in the tongue groove, again to the count of seven. Hold the breath for one count, then exhale slowly through both nostrils to the count of seven. Repeat this cycle sixteen times.

♉ TAURUS
The Bull

(April 20 through May 20)

Planetary Ruler: Venus (♀)
Related to: Throat, neck, Eustachian tubes, cervical vertebrae.
Your Body Needs: Foods containing sulphate of soda.
You Should Develop: Optimism and flexibility.
You Should Avoid: Stubbornness and self-indulgence.

In most astrological textbooks, you will find Taurus, the second sign of the zodiac, characterized as earthly, melancholy, fixed, negative, and fruitful—the night-house of Venus.

While these are important key words for the experienced astrologer, unless you have been instructed in the art of erecting and interpreting a horoscope, they will not provide a very clear picture of your Taurean make-up, physical and mental.

As the Taurine symbol of your sign suggests, you are a peace-loving creature unless threatened or enraged. Once provoked, however, you will attack any enemy regardless of size or strength.

Physically, you possess great vitality and endurance, but your energy is not self-generating, as in the case of the fire and air signs; it requires some stimulation from persons and conditions outside yourself. You are most readily influenced by associates who have the fixed signs —Leo, Scorpio, and Aquarius—prominent in their natal charts.

Planets positioned in these signs in your own birth map will tend to affect the parts of the body usually assigned to their dominance, such as heart, sex organs, and ankles.

You have a deep-seated fear of disease and are very susceptible to negative suggestions regarding your health, often preferring to believe the worst about your condition. You should cultivate a more optimistic outlook, bearing in mind that natives of your sign usually exhibit a formidable resistance to most diseases.

The health problems you are most likely to encounter during your lifetime are: throat infections; diseases involving the larynx, neck, ears, sex glands (by reflex action from Scorpio); diphtheria; goiter; quinsy; asthma; sinusitis; and disabilities stemming from over-indulgence in rich foods.

Common complaints, such as colds and sore throats, which natives of the other Sun signs soon overcome, may prove more serious to you because they affect the areas of your greatest sensitivity and weakness. For that reason, you should not neglect early treatment. If severe inflammation occurs, you should rest in bed for a day or two, applying warmth to the affected parts and faithfully taking whatever medication your doctor prescribes.

If treated early, at the onset of infection, such conditions will often respond to inhalation of warm vapor from hot water in which medicated oil or salve has been dissolved.

As a Taurean, the most important thing for you to remember is never to treat lightly an infection of the throat or of the trachea. Such a condition could become chronic.

Getting adequate physical exercise is of utmost importance to you, if you would avoid circulatory problems which plague Taureans who lead sedentary lives.

YOUR PERSONALITY INVENTORY

The impressions and experiences of early childhood—important in shaping the adult character of all of us—are especially indelible in the Taurean's life. The conditions of home environment, the feelings of love, trust, and respect for the grown-ups in charge of your care and education—all have a lasting effect on your personality.

The most outstanding feature of your character is tenacity of purpose. Whatever you undertake, you pursue with great determination and industry, sometimes with obstinacy.

You have been endowed with considerable mental ability and, unless adverse planetary aspects give testimony to the contrary, you usually apply yourself seriously to study. Your patience and perseverance can mean high academic honors if you are following a formal course of education, or the satisfaction of personal accomplishment if you are pursuing a program of self-improvement.

Where affairs of the heart are concerned, you are capable of great tenderness and affection. Although a devoted spouse, you are not always easy to live with, chiefly because your mate never knows exactly what may set you off on a rampage. Not that these outbursts are frequent; most of the time you are even-tempered and considerate. But when you feel that you are being driven against your will, or when your domestic or personal domain is threatened, you lower your head and charge, or sullenly paw the carpet.

You are intensely loyal to friends, and ever ready to lend them financial help when they are in need.

You are extremely sensitive to psychic currents and emotional influences around you, even though some astrologers do not associate such extrasensory perception with an Earth sign.

Because you are thus unconsciously affected by the

thoughts of others, you ought always to make important decisions when you are alone—preferably during a solitary walk or in some natural setting such as a garden or a park.

To sum up:

The influence of Taurus expresses itself through determination, energy, gentleness, friendship, domesticity, and benevolence. Venus, your planetary ruler, endows you with a pleasant, musical voice and gives an appreciation for beauty in all the arts.

Dr. Howard Cornell lists as the pathological qualities of your sign: anger, brooding, love of luxury, excessive stubbornness, and uncontrolled emotions. These traits can cause illness when progressed planetary aspects trigger energy potentials in your horoscope.

YOUR GUIDE TO DIET

Many of the health problems commonly associated with Taurus can be prevented or corrected by proper diet.

Your natural fondness for starchy foods, sweets, and pastries may give you an early start on overweight, a trend you'll find difficult to reverse in middle age. Aside from esthetic considerations (and most Taureans are somewhat vain about their personal appearance), the adipose tissue you accumulate can result in circulatory troubles. Try to eat less, even though, unless afflictions in your Fourth and Sixth Houses give contrary testimonies, you rarely have digestive disorders. It is well to remember that with your sign (as with all the others of the zodiac) anger, inharmony, and unpleasant discussions during meals will result in any number of psychosomatic ills, including ulcers and bladder disorders.

The cell-salt of your sign is sulphate of soda. It is needed to control the amount of water retained by your body. A deficiency of the salt will result in swelling of tissues owing to accumulation of water in the body. Foods which contain sulphate of soda include spinach, beets,

Swiss chard, cucumber, cauliflower, onions, cabbage, pumpkin, and radishes.

You should also make sure that your diet supplies you with an adequate amount of iodine to insure the proper functioning of your thyroid gland, thus preventing goiter, to which Taureans are sometimes prone. The best common sources of iodine are: most salt-water fish and seafood and iodized salt. Iodine requirement is usually greatest during childhood and adolescence; and for women during pregnancy and at menopause.

Herbs most commonly associated with Taurus are sage, yarrow, barberry, coltsfoot, sorrel, and celandine.

After the age of 45, Taureans may sometimes find it beneficial to their over-all health to supplement their regular diet with vitamins A and E.

YOGIC BREATHING FOR TAURUS

Time: 9 to 11 A.M.
Place: Garden, park, open country.
Duration of practice: 15 minutes to a half hour.
Technique: Take a leisurely stroll through a park, if possible. If you live in a city where no such retreat is conveniently nearby, walk about your own neighborhood. Try to develop a feeling of detachment from your man-made surroundings (not at busy street intersections, of course!) and to enjoy the beauty of nature, even if it is only the changing aspect of the sky or a distant grove of trees.

As you amble along, slowly and deeply inhale through both nostrils to the count of seven. Hold your breath for two seconds (i.e., while you count to two). Then exhale through the mouth to the count of seven. With your lungs empty, wait for two seconds, then inhale once more to the count of seven. Repeat the cycle 16 times.

The whole exercise should be done without pressure

or force. You will soon learn from practice how much air is required to fill your lungs without discomfort.

If your daily schedule makes the preferred time of practice difficult to fit in, you can do the exercise at any time that suits your convenience.

After a week or two, you will find that both the yogic *pranayama* and the physical exercise will begin to yield results in improved coordination of nerves and muscle, better circulation, and greater vitality.

♊ GEMINI
The Twins

(May 22 through June 21)

Planetary Ruler: Mercury (☿)
Related to: Shoulders, arms, lungs, nervous system.
Your Body Needs: Foods containing potassium chloride.
You Should Develop: Tranquility, self-discipline, goal-directed action.
You Should Avoid: Nervous exhaustion; scattering your forces.

A typical Geminian I know, working at a typical Gemini job—that of feature writer for a metropolitan newspaper—began experiencing shooting pains on the right side of his head. His first thought was that his trouble might be mental. So he consulted not an ordinary general practitioner, but a prominent psychiatrist.

"I figured that if it was just jumpy nerves, a good head-shrinker could diagnose my condition as well as a plain neurologist," my friend said afterward. "At the same time, I could have him check over my battered psyche to see whether there were any premonitory symptoms of an impending crack-up."

After a thorough examination, which included everything from an electroencephalogram to a Rorschach ink-blot test, the doctor rendered his diagnosis in two words:

"Chronic alertness."

That gave my friend's colleagues down at the press club a hearty laugh, but the fact was that the psychiatrist had pinpointed the Twin's trouble with dead-on accuracy.

He had, at the same time, made a correct general diagnosis for everybody related to the third sign of the zodiac. Almost without exception, you Geminians seem to be constantly wide-awake and mentally in overdrive.

To the untrained observer (and that includes a great many astrologers), it appears that you are afraid of missing something. Ostensibly, you want to go everywhere, do everything, read every book, and discuss every subject known to man—all in the span of time it takes most of your friends just to get started on one thing.

There is more going on inside your complex, computer-swift mind than a mere desire to "do it while the doing is good," however. The outpouring of nervous energy and the ever-shifting focus of your attention stems from a finely balanced sensitivity, which in the esoteric astrology of India is described by a term which means "open to knowing."

Evangeline Adams, whose assessment of Geminians had its blind spots, recognized this psychic receptivity, which she called "an excellent token of artistry."

"People with this position of the Sun are likely to hear more, to see more than the average men," she wrote. "They are open to impressions, even the most delicate, and, where Mercury assists, are able to record them with exquisite fidelity."

This incessant state of super-awareness is understandably very exhausting to the nervous system. For that reason, the Twin requires more sleep than the average person, as well as daily outdoor exercise to stimulate circulation and to strengthen the lungs (one of the potentially weak parts of the Geminian physique).

Although Gemini is usually considered the strongest of the common signs, the natives of this sign are not robust unless some of the more invigorating planets are present

57

and well aspected on the ascendant and in the Sixth House of their natal charts.

Max Heindel says that the Twin is often careless about his health and that on that account "we find more tubercular patients among Gemini people than among people of any of the other eleven signs."

(The Brotherhood of Light's 30-year research reports indicate that Saturn, Neptune, Jupiter, and Pluto were prominent in the birth charts of all the 100 tubercular patients analyzed. On the other hand, Mercury, the planetary ruler of Gemini, was prominent in 96 percent of the nativities of persons suffering nervous breakdown.)

Other diseases to which Gemini people are more than ordinarily susceptible include: bronchitis, asthma, pneumonia, neuritis, sluggish liver, abscesses in the lungs, skin ailments, and, when their Mercury is afflicted, mental disorders.

Some authorities on the subject of medical astrology (Dr. H. L. Cornell among them) say that Gemini, being a dual-bodied sign, makes the native liable to suffer from two diseases at the same time.

Since many of your health problems have their origin in the mental depression which results when you are suppressed in your desire for intellectual expression, or are subjected to the monotony of unchanging daily routine, you should seek employment which will provide variety and frequent change of scene.

GEMINI'S PERSONALITY DIMENSIONS

As already indicated, Gemini, your sign is one of the least clearly understood of the celestial twelve.

Sidney Omarr, whose outstanding accuracy in diagnosing character by astrology owes much to his independent, first-hand research, attributes the confusion to the fact that the typical Geminian is multifaceted.

He ventures the opinion that a survey of the Twin's

friends and associates would show that each person holds a different picture, a different description, a different concept of the Geminian. "You are not easy to know because, in a way, you are so many persons rolled into one."

Astrologers who repeat only what they have read in traditional texts describe your type as clever, quick-witted, curious, often fickle, pleasure-loving, and irresponsible.

"There is not much warmth in a Geminian," flatly states one writer, who has probably been rebuffed (or what is more likely, ignored by one. Another generalizes: "Gemini natives will overwhelm you with warm affection one minute, and turn into an emotional iceberg the next."

British astrologer Jeff Mayo writes (apparently with approval) that it has even been suggested that the chattering, imitative, restless monkey would be a better symbol for the sign than that of the heavenly Twins.

Applying these traits of the negative, lower type of sign to everyone belonging to that zodiacal group is one of the practices which have brought astrology into disrepute. Are the great music of Grieg, Stravinsky, and Wagner; the immortal poetry of Whitman and Tennyson; the literary work of Emerson, Hawthorne, and Hardy; and the philosophical contributions of Leibnitz and Pascal, the work of chattering, imitative, restless monkeys?

It is true that *most* Geminians do talk a lot. But, unless they respond to adverse influences in their planetary configuration, they usually have something worthwhile to say. They should avoid interrupting others, or showing impatience and rudeness to the more plodding types.

The effect you Geminians have on others is rarely apparent, even to you. But very often, a passing word, phrase, or observation, which you have snatched from the psychic magma around you, given voice and then quickly forgotten, may make a lasting impression on one of your hearers. The reason is that you are a messenger of the gods—a kind of spiritual middleman. You have the ability to lift the spirits of people. An entire gathering sometimes will light up when you enter the room, bringing with you an infectious enthusiasm, gaiety, and exciting conversation.

Authorities on occult astrology have said that, when a Geminian first comes into the life of a person belonging to any of the other eleven signs, it should be taken as an index that there are changes in prospect. Thierens, in his *Elements of Esoteric Astrology,* adds: "It may also be that he will appear the one who is going to bring out either the merits of your work or its weaknesses."

In whatever his role, the Geminian should exercise the tact and lightness of touch of which he is capable. He should always bear in mind that a cutting remark or a sarcastic witticism may show off his brilliant mind, but it is not fulfilling his cosmic responsibility as a *communicator* of constructive ideas which help build the morale of those in his immediate environment.

It is in the ancient language of alchemy that the deepest nature and function of the Twin is demonstrated. If you have ever handled quicksilver (the common name for Mercury, the planetary significator of Gemini), you will better understand the elusive, protean character of the sign.

Writing of the hermetic or alchemical tradition of astrology, the late Elbert Benjamine said of Mercury (your planetary ruler):

"A little quicksilver spilled in the laboratory and its drops are everywhere—elusive, quick-moving, and of brilliant silver-white luster. . . . Mercury is a metal of wonderful penetration. Its particles readily find egress through substances that are impervious to other metals. It may be strained through buckskin or even through a chamois-skin bag, and the minutely divided particles will again immediately unite, even as man's thoughts penetrate the inmost recesses of nature and after their separate work of exploration, collect again to become a conviction."

In sum: The function of Gemini is the relation between self and substance. For that purpose, you need adequate sunshine, rest, plenty of light and air, and a constantly revolving landscape—mental as well as physical. Change

60

is as necessary for you as the air you breathe. You were never intended to make your home in a pigeonhole, figuratively speaking. For you to do so will quickly undermine your health and bring on illness, which can easily be avoided by change of residence, employment, or—God forbid—marriage partner.

GEMINI GUIDE TO DIET

Few Geminians are to be found working at jobs which involve heavy, manual labor. Instead, they usually turn to employment that requires a quick mind or nimble, skillful hands.

Accordingly, if you were born between May 20 and June 21, you should make sure that your daily diet includes foods that will nourish exhausted nerves, increase vitality, and regulate fibrin in the blood. This means that in general you should favor a protein diet that includes lean meat, fish, eggs, cheese, nuts, and soybeans.

Calcium foods are also especially important to Geminians, because calcium helps to calm jumpy nerves. Yogurt, milk, turnip greens, and kale are common sources of this mineral. If it appears that you are not assimilating enough calcium from your food, a dietary supplement in the form of bone meal or calcium tablets may be beneficial. Bear in mind that vitamin D is needed to aid absorption of calcium.

The cell-salt of Gemini is potassium chloride, which is liberally supplied by green beans, asparagus, beets, carrots, cauliflower, sweet corn, celery, apricots, peaches, plums, and pineapple. Some of these foods should form a part of your daily menu.

Among the herbs which Geminians will find helpful are comfrey, vervain, red clover, and licorice.

Back in 1943, David Harold Fink, M.D., wrote a book called *Release from Nervous Tension*. In it the physician examines the causes and effects of nervous stress, and offers a simple program for overcoming it. The book has gone through many printings and is probably still available at your bookseller's. If you can obtain a copy (your public library may have one), you should read it carefully, since you, perhaps more than any other member of the zodiacal family, can profit by Dr. Fink's analysis and advice.

YOGA FOR THE TWINS

Time: Between 10 A.M. and noon.
Place: Hilltop or well-ventilated room.
Duration of Practice: 6 minutes.
Techniques: Seated comfortably but erect, in a straight chair, close your eyes, relax, and allow your thoughts to run on without any conscious direction from you. Mentally step aside, as it were, and permit your stream of consciousness to flow without restraint. You become an observer of the passing show. And what a show it sometimes becomes! You may be surprised at some of the ideas or images that flash across the screen of awareness—thoughts which rise out of the depths of your unconscious mind.

During the first few days of practice, you may find it difficult to release yourself, to surrender your thoughts. But, in time, calmness will come.

After a few moments, start to monitor your breathing. Inhale gently as you count to seven; pause one count; and exhale to the count of seven. Repeat this cycle approximately 12 times (the exact number doesn't matter). Then, closing your right nostril with your forefinger, inhale through the left nostril, again to the count of seven. Hold one count and then close the left nostril and exhale through the right. Continue the cycle in this way, breathing in through one nostril and exhaling through the opposite side.

This somewhat simplified *pranayama* has as its objective what yogis call purification of the nerves. It should be con-

62

tinued for three minutes or more, but not so long that you begin to feel giddy or lightheaded.

If you practice faithfully, even once a day (in India, where life moves at a slower pace, beginners repeat it five times daily), you will eventually begin to feel a pleasant sense of calmness and confidence.

You may even become sufficiently interested to go more fully into the whole system of *hatha yoga*. The Twin is rarely content with knowing merely part of a subject once his interest or curiosity is aroused.

♋ CANCER
The Crab

(June 22 through July 21)

Planetary Ruler: Moon (☽)
Related to: Epigastric region, breasts, stomach, elbow joints.
Your Body Needs: Foods containing calcium fluoride (also called fluoride of lime).
You Should Develop: Self-confidence and emotional balance.
You Should Avoid: Moodiness, chip-on shoulder attitude, and over-eating.

The Greeks had a word for your astrological keynote: *skiamachia*—shadow-boxing. You are forever battling against phantoms which have no substance in the real world, but are bodiless entities, and ideas, fathered by your emotion and given birth in your fertile imagination.

That all sounds like slightly overblown rhetoric, but don't shrug it off too hastily. Mental images can sometimes be as cruel and tyrannical as though they existed in tangible form. Tibetan mystics call such thought-forms *tulpas* and assure us that they are capable of doing considerable mischief, if not controlled.

In her fascinating account of *Magic and Mystery in Tibet,* Madame David-Neel tells how she created an imaginary monk, who became so independent and unresponsive to her will that he gradually assumed a form visible to others, and actually posed a threat to her well-being. He eventually had to be ritualistically dispatched.

The typical Cancerian rarely finds the private world of his own making a satisfactory one. The result is inner conflict and unfounded suspicions, which cause tension and the physical disorders brought on by tension: nervous indigestion, ulcers, gastritis, stomach disorders, and poor elimination.

Many, if not all, of these health troubles can be avoided by cultivating the opposite emotions from those which engendered them in the first place. Instead of suspicion, the Crab (Carroll Righter prefers to call you a Moonchild) should develop trust; instead of worry and apprehension, optimism and cheerfulness; instead of grudges, a spirit of forgiveness.

Easier said than done? Of course. Especially when you feel the Moon's pull, as that swift-moving planet passes through its various phases, affecting all of us, but you in particular.

Linda Goodman, in her delightful Arien romp through the zodiac, observes, "There's a touch of moon madness in every Cancerian." If you want to enjoy good health and a rewarding sense of personal fulfillment, turn that touch of lunacy to good account in one or more of the creative arts. First-decanate Cancerians (born between June 21 and July 30) especially have dramatic talent and a potential for poetic expression.

While Cancer is generally considered one of the two weakest signs of the zodiac (the other being Pisces), if the Sun is well-aspected, rising and elevated at the time of birth, it will greatly strengthen the physical constitution and impart a vitality which will make you resistant to disease and give you recuperative powers that Cancerians with weaker natal charts don't have.

The Moon's influence over your health is more acutely felt in infancy and childhood than in your mature years. However, unless other planetary positions strongly intervene, all through life the lunar cycles will be reflected in recurring illnesses, and in critical days during periods when you are sick.

Older astrologers believed that female babies born during an eclipse of the Moon or at the time of a new Moon were likely to die at birth or a short time afterward. This view is no longer held by most authorities in the field of medical astrology; but both aspects are still believed to exercise an adverse effect on the health picture of girls born at those times.

Because of personal disappointments, hurts, or worries you may at times be tempted to drown your sorrows in alcohol. Be on your guard against such overindulgence as a means of escape; they will only lead to further emotional disturbances and ill health.

The position of the Moon at your moment of birth will determine to a large extent which Cancerian weaknesses (and strengths!) will receive the greatest emphasis in your life. However, it can be taken as a general rule that lowered vitality resulting from emotional upsets or morbid mental states characterizes the over-all pathological quality of your Sun sign.

PSYCHOLOGICAL PROFILE

The words most often used by astrologers—ancient and modern—to describe the Cancer-born are: sensitive, timid, imaginative, domestic, pleasure-loving, capricious, and frugal.

These are broad generalizations, of course, and not all of the traits here cited will apply to you, unless you happen to be extraordinarily typical of the sign.

In the main, however, these key words serve to provide a rather accurate psychological profile of the Crab.

According to esoteric astrology, which explores the deeper cosmic purpose and meaning of each sign, Cancer is related to the life-principle of the organism, and embodies its growth potential.

You Cancerians have strong protective and maternal instincts, because you have stewardship over the portals between the seen and unseen, the entranceway through which souls must pass into physical embodiment.

Although normally somewhat shy until you are sure you're among friends, you can be a great show-off once the ice is broken. This urge to put on a performance stems partly from a deeply felt need for recognition and approval, and partly from a sincere desire to see others laugh and enjoy themselves.

This seemingly paradoxical behavior—going from social timidity to forms of extrovertive expression—carries through into other phases of your character as well. Left to your own devices and natural bent, you can easily become an idle dreamer and visionary. But when aroused to action by the sharp realities of daily experience, you are capable of great energy and tenacity of purpose.

In fact, the Crab is noted for thrift and industry ('tis the ruling sign of Scotland, mon!) and is reputed to be a shrewd bargainer who knows how to get the best of any trade.

Usually you are a patriotic citizen who values your country's traditions of freedom and justice and are ready to defend them if you feel they are threatened. Few Cancerians are to be found among today's flag-burners. They are often politically liberal, but rarely extremist.

When Cancer-born Louis "Sachmo" Armstrong was asked during World War II why he, a Negro, was willing to fight for a country that denied his race full civil rights at home, he replied: "There's nothing wrong with my country that this guy Hitler can fix."

A prominent feature of your character is love of home and family. Nothing can be more upsetting to the Crab than inharmonious conditions in his private household. If he feels that his mate does not love him, or that he has been slighted by other members of the family, he is inclined to sulk, and to suffer digestive troubles as a result.

You are very susceptible to psychic influences and are attracted to the occult world. Your interest may lie in ESP, spiritualism, or some other form of contact with the supernatural.

A word of caution here: Be sure the individuals or group with whom you associate yourself in such activities have the highest aims and are of good character. A close rapport with the lower levels of psychism could be ruinous for you.

In choosing a congenial vocation, you should seek employment in which your sensitive nature will be an asset rather than a liability. Because you are amiable, sympathetic, and popular, you could be a successful politician. Other ideal Cancerian careers: advertising, hotel management, sales work, theatrical artists, restaurant operation, brokerage, antique dealership, and talent agency.

DIET AND VITAMIN SUPPLEMENTS

Cancerians are known for their excellent cooking and the pride they take in a well-laden, epicurean table. This trait is greatly appreciated by your family and friends, who are always glad for the opportunity to sit down to one of your gourmet spreads.

The trouble is, you have an appetite for good food which matches your skill in preparing it. You are inclined to find rich pastries, ice cream, and other sweets particularly irresistible. You should try to control this tendency to overeat, which is especially strong when you are under some kind of mental strain or on an emotional binge. Remember that the stomach and alimentary system are the weakest areas of your physical make-up. Don't overtax them.

You should avoid an overabundance of sugar, starchy foods, and fat in your diet. Most—at least a great many—Cancerians begin to put on weight fairly early in life, a predisposition that often leads to an imbalance in the essential metabolism of the body, as well as to edema (swelling of tissues due to water retention).

Your basic diet should lean heavily toward proteins, and should include a certain amount of seafood to insure an adequate intake of iodine. In addition, you require a variety of fruits, vegetables, and leafy greens.

The cell-salt of Cancer is calcium fluoride, commonly referred to as fluoride of lime. A deficiency of this mineral can cause varicose veins, prolapsed muscles, tooth decay, and weakened eyesight.

The following foods are the best sources of this important Cancerian nutrient: milk and cheese or yogurt, kale, watercress, savoy and red cabbage, pumpkin, onions, oranges, lemons, egg yolks, raisins, and rye bread.

For an excellent noonday sandwich for Cancerians who are on a weight-reducing diet, mix finely grated onion with cottage cheese, sprinkle with celery seed, and spread on a slice of rye bread or rye wafer.

Some of the herbs traditionally associated with your sign are saxifrage, white poppy, chickweed, pellitory, wild clary, purslane, and rosemary.

You may find it desirable to fortify your diet with vitamins E and those of the B-complex. Orthodox medical opinion to the contrary, vitamins derived from natural sources are better than synthetic ones.

YOGA FOR CANCERIANS

All yogic breathing should involve muscular contractions to assist and control the diaphragm, producing an effortless flow of air into and out of the lungs.

In the case of the following exercise, which is a modification of a technique known as *kapala bhati* in India, correct muscular control is of paramount importance.

Time: Morning and evening. (Sun must be above the horizon.)

Place: Anywhere you will have privacy and fresh air.

Duration of Practice: 5 minutes.

Technique: Stand erect, facing the Sun, feet firmly planted on the floor or ground. Close your eyes and, with your shoulders thrown back, breathe slowly and rhythmically in and out, filling the lungs, but not to the point of discomfort.

After practicing this preliminary inhalation-exhalation discipline for a period of about three minutes, place your hands on your hips, with the thumbs thrust forward, resting along the lines where the legs are joined to the torso.

Using the abdominal muscles as a kind of bellows, breathe rapidly but lightly in and out (through the nostrils, not through the mouth). Contract the muscles as you exhale, forcing the air out, and expand them when you inhale. *Do not perform the exercise too strenuously or too fast; and do not exert excessive pressure.*

At first, do not practice longer than a minute. This time can be extended to two or three minutes over a period of several months. After daily performance for six months, discontinue the bellows part of the exercise and continue with the rhythmic deep breathing.

The bellows praxis may be resumed at infrequent intervals, when you feel the need for stimulating the function of the digestive system or of the lungs. However, it should never be practiced when you are physically tired or in ill health.

♌ LEO
The Lion

(July 22 through August 21)

Planetary Ruler: Sun (☉)
Related to: Heart, gall bladder, dorsal region of back and spine.
Your Body Needs: Foods containing magnesium phosphate.
You Should Develop: Tact and deliberation.
You Should Avoid: Conceit, haste, and excitement.

The Sun—that blazing, golden star around which the planets of our system revolve, the source of all vital power and the regulator of life forces on earth—passes through Leo, the sign it rules from July 22 through August 21.

You who are fortunate enough to be born during that period are endowed with tremendous physical energy and recuperative powers. Your whole life is characterized by dynamic intensity of purpose and action.

Leo represents the heart of man, as well as the heart of creation. The principal diseases of the sign are ailments related to that vital organ and to its function. They include, among others: arteriosclerosis and degenerative heart disease, angina pectoris, carditis, aneurysms, and tachycardia.

Leo people may also experience brief illnesses characterized by high fever; or be plagued with back pains, spinal troubles, and locomotor ataxia, depending upon what planetary afflictions, if any, are indicated in their horoscopes.

Your place in the celestial scheme of things makes you prone to attack in your youth by rheumatic fever, measles, and meningitis (if you are exposed to overcrowding, as in a military barracks).

Leo is not usually subject to chronic, lingering illnesses, but to acute disorders which strike suddenly and are of short duration.

Keeping in mind, no doubt, Leo's fervent zest in both work and play, Dr. Cornell adds to the sign's pathological qualities "diseases resulting from excesses, pleasures, amusements, love affairs, passional excesses, etc."

The basic rule for you to observe to keep your good health is to control the outflow of solar energy which you possess in such abundance. In a word, moderation, insofar as moderation is possible for the exuberant Lion.

You need a fair amount of restorative sleep, whether you get it in eight-hour stretches, in cat-nap intervals, or during an afternoon siesta. Recent medical research has shown that, in addition to undermining health, prolonged loss of sleep can seriously impair a person's ability to carry on any activity satisfactorily, or safely to accept important responsibility.

Science was merely confirming what conventional wisdom had always thought. Don Quixote's esquire, Sancho Panza, said it with peasant simplicity: "God bless the man who first invented sleep."

THE LEONINE PROFILE

Just as all astrologers traditionally have had many bad things to say about Scorpio, they have been equally unanimous in praising the proud, bossy Lion.

Leo is forceful, commanding, forthright, honest, generous, constructive, affectionate, loyal, romantic, astute,

72

the possessor of deep emotions, kind, and cheerfully cock-sure. The endless lexicon goes on and on, sounding like Roget on an ego trip.

"You think big; you aspire to the heights in your profession." (Righter)

"You are a good organizer and must 'boss the show.'" (Tucker)

"The nature is excessively proud and incapable of meanness." (Adams)

"You are gregarious, generous, and idealistic." (Omarr)

"He is reliable, not afraid to make decisions and abide by them." (Gleadow)

Linda Goodman, who must have studied an uncaged member of the species at *very* close range, got one of her gushy spells when she came to summarize the sign. She rhapsodized:

"Brimming over with fun and generosity, the gay, affectionate lion prances in a field of poppies when his Sun is high in the sky—and the dice he throws with confidence bear the numbers one and four. Leo proudly wears a topaz for luck, then pushes it too far, but he has a true inner dignity and grace that lets him carry his misfortunes with courage. The warm, yellow rays of his cheerful hope deepen to orange in the sunset's glow, and his nights are bright with a thousand stars."

Ahem!

Certainly, no Leo would disagree with any of the foregoing appraisal of his character. That is exactly the way he views himself. And the fact is, as broad generalizations, the statements are all true.

Leo is the sign of royalty, and the Lion behaves accordingly. Even his amorous favors are dispensed with a certain air of condescension. Leonian Mae West had a long and successful career playing herself on screen and stage, always supported by one or more young male admirers.

Some years ago, the following story, possibly apocryphal, made the rounds in Hollywood. It illustrates perfectly the Leo life style:

At a birthday party for the late great humorist Will Rogers, when the presents were opened, there was a mysterious little package from Mae West. When unwrapped, it revealed an empty wrist-watch case, with a note inside.

Of course, the curious gift aroused a great deal of interest among the guests (as it was intended to do), who urged Rogers to share the message with them. He did. It read:

"Come up and see me sometime and I'll give you the works."

That famous *double-entendre* and Miss West's regal, but highly suggestive, delivery of it are both typical of Leo. The Lion loves the spotlight, but only in the aloof role of a monarch at a state function.

Before you start to purr (as Leo always does when exposed to flattery, let us look at the negative side of the sign; because, although hard to believe, there *are* unevolved types among natives of the sign who still bear the mark of the beast.

When afflicted, Leo may be overweeningly arrogant rather than proud, brutish rather than merely strong, sensual rather than amorous, patronizing rather than sympathetic and warmhearted.

Although he is never deliberately cruel, his disregard for the rights of others can lead to the worst kind of oppression and tyranny if he is in an official or executive position. Thierens warns: "Nature made them all incorrigible beasts of prey."

Even the noblest of the breed may be given to spells of laziness and procrastination. Leo's natural boldness and confidence in his lucky stars sometimes lead to compulsive gambling, either on the stock market, in business, or at cards and dice.

DIET AND CELL-SALT

Leo should adopt a nutritional regimen which is high in protein and fairly low in sugar and starches. Recent scientific studies tend to support the view that saturated fats also play an important role in the development of atherosclerosis (hardening and narrowing of the arteries).

Since the Lion is predisposed by cosmic conditioning to heart disease and related disorders, it is prudent for him to avoid contributing factors such as overweight, stress, and improper diet. Warning signals that you need to improve your living habits include shortness of breath, a sharp, short pain under the breastbone, dizziness, or nausea.

Foods which supply adequate protein and help correct poor circulation include lean meats, game, fowl, yogurt, cheese, eggs, and soybeans.

The Leo cell-salt is magnesium phosphate. It is essential for restoration of nervous energy, which the Lion expends so lavishly, and in firming up the muscles and skeletal structure. It also stimulates the digestive and excretory functions, assists in the formation of albumin in the blood, and maintains the blood's natural fluidity.

Valuable sources of magnesium sulphate are almonds, rye, lettuce, apples, plums, figs, lemons, coconut, cucumber, blueberries, walnuts, and onions.

Leos are rarely heavy drinkers, which is a good thing, considering the ill effects they are likely to experience from overindulgence. However, red wine taken with dinner will be beneficial, if consumed in moderation.

The vitamins most important to your sign are C and E. When possible, it is best to obtain these from natural rather than synthetic sources. Vitamin C is supplied by citrus fruits, tomatoes, rose hips, watercress, cantaloupe, and strawberries. In normal circumstances, your body's need for vitamin E can be met if you include in your daily diet wheat germ, lettuce, and vegetable oils (especially soybean oil).

Healing herbs associated with Leo are dill, fennel, parsley, mint, and dandelion.

YOGA FOR THE LION

The practice of deep breathing, beneficial to natives of every sign in the zodiac when adapted to their individual place in the Sun, is especially important to those strongly influenced by Leo. The reason for this is that, if practiced at the prescribed time, the air you inhale will be charged with solar energy, which you need to revitalize your whole system.

Today, when a significant segment of the medical profession has joined the American Heart Association and American Cancer Society in urging *all* cigarette smokers to "kick" the habit, it will not seem unreasonable to recommend that Leo join "the unhooked generation."

Not only will you lessen the possibility of an early heart attack or stroke, but the following exercise will be much more effective.

Time: Noon to 1 p.m. and 2 to 3 p.m.
Place: Secluded outdoor area, in full sunlight when possible.
Duration: 10 minutes.
Technique: Stand or sit erect, with shoulders thrown back and spine straight. Place the fingers of your right hand around your left wrist in the position used by doctors and nurses to take the pulse. After a little experimentation, you will feel the pulse beats quite distinctly.

Now slowly and deeply inhale to the count of seven of your own pulse beats. Count seven beats as you exhale. Continue this rhythmic respiratory cycle about 67 times during the first few weeks of practice, then gradually extend it to 200.

The breath should flow smoothly in and out, the bellows action of the lungs aided by contraction and expansion of the abdominal muscles.

♍ VIRGO
The Virgin

(August 22 through September 22)

Planetary Ruler: Mercury (☿)
Related to: Abdominal area, small intestines, gastrointestinal system.
Your Body Needs: Foods containing potassium sulphate.
You Should Develop: A broader outlook; greater variety of interests.
You Should Avoid: Being hypercritical; involvement in trivia.

As a native of the sixth sign of the zodiac, associated with the Sixth House, you have more than an ordinary interest in matters which concern health, diet, and hygiene. In fact, your interest in these subjects can easily become almost an obsession with you.

There are several reasons for this. First is your inborn fear of disease. Add to that the fact that you are inclined to brood over the slightest symptoms and even to identify yourself closely with the illnesses of those around you.

To put it bluntly, as Manly Hall once observed, Virgoans "can ail quite a bit without being sick."

While you are the most robust type of the zodiacal twelve, if you will exercise just the ordinary precautions in guarding your health, you will probably outlive your more able-bodied associates.

At the same time, take this word of caution to heart: The Virgo person can easily become an invalid, especially in advanced years, as a result of allowing himself to be caught in the grip of despair. Because of this negative attitude, your physician finds it difficult to heal and cure you successfully. It is vitally important for you, early in life, to learn to think of your body in terms of health and well-being rather than as a potential victim of disease. Try to generate a more positive kind of warmth in your relations with others, instead of the negative kind of rapport that comes through having them sympathize with you because of poor health, fancied or real.

The Virgo native has his personal pharmacy near him at all times, even when traveling. His astonishing collection of pills, potions, and medicinal preparations will pretty well cover the field of *Materia Medica*. A Virgo friend comes in very handy when you have a headache, acid indigestion, toothache, or backache, and the corner pharmacy is closed. Not only will he have a remedy for your pain, but a generous amount of sincere sympathy to go along with it. It is this trait which has led most astrologers to place the nursing profession high on the list of vocations suitable to the sign.

Actually, unless planetary configurations modify the typical Virgo geniture, attending the sick is not a good occupation for natives of this sign. As previously pointed out, they have a tendency to emphasize *too* strongly with the patient, to the detriment of their own well-being. As a Virgoan you must turn your thoughts *away* from disease, not toward it.

Among the nostrums you should remove from your medicine chest (or keep only for the use of non-Virgo friends) are strong proprietary remedies for acid indigestion, and harsh laxatives. Your bowels and intestines are more than ordinarily sensitive to such drugs, and their habitual use could do you serious harm.

You should bear in mind that a great many of your physical ailments are the result of slowly built-up nervous tensions, which find release in this way. It follows, then, that your over-all health will improve if you will learn to "let go," to cultivate an inner sense of detachment to match the exterior look of cool aloofness you often wear.

Ailments to which the Virgo native may be prone are: digestive disorders and diarrhea, obstructions in the bowels, peritonitis, tapeworm, typhoid, colitis, appendicitis, and hernia.

VIRGO ON THE INSIDE

From the foregoing analysis, one might conclude that the typical Virgo native is a sort of namby-pamby weakling. Nothing could be farther from the truth.

Your strength is not of the body, but of the mind, and your world is a mental world. Like Gemini, your planetary ruler is Mercury but, unlike the airy Twin, you express the colder side of the heavenly Messenger, yours being a negative, moist, earthy sign.

In your reaction to the world around you and to the events taking place in it, you are deeply analytical, reserved, and cautious. You find it next to impossible to experience love for the opposite sex in a passionate sense, because complete self-surrender is abhorrent to you. At the same time, you have a compassionate larger love for mankind as a whole and a desire to save and to improve humanity.

A perfectionist in all you undertake, you carefully sift and classify every minute detail of any enterprise or course of action. This trait, plus your dependability and ingenuity in carrying out orders, makes you the type of employee much sought by large firms and executives whose business involves elaborate planning and systematic procedures, or requires superior powers of discernment.

Virgo people whose birth charts show serious afflictions of the malefics may experience a gnawing discontent with their surroundings and lot in life, which will prompt them to move from one place of employment or residence to another. But their hopes are never quite fulfilled, and the ensuing cynicism may result in tensions that tie their stomachs into knots, thus undermining their general health.

Even when your sign is well-aspected, Virgo, you should guard against heavy physical exertion which will put a strain on your abdominal muscles. On the other hand, any exercise or activity which will tend to strengthen or relax those sore muscles can be highly beneficial.

Your approach to marriage is often an intellectual one, which your life partner may find difficult to understand. Still, your selfless devotion to the home and family and your moral rectitude go far toward making up for the lack of hearts-and-flowers romance. It is important for you to choose your mate carefully, though (and of course you will; you're careful about everything), because domestic inharmony is a prime source of illness for Virgo.

To conclude your personality inventory on a positive note, let us summarize the virtues typical of your sign. They are quite impressive:

You possess a penetrating, alert mind. You are studious, precise, factual, quick to learn. Your inner urge for order and efficiency manifests itself in tidiness and personal neatness. On the academic level, you are capable of outstanding achievement, especially in the fields of science, and branches of knowledge which require a highly developed faculty of critical analysis.

The most healthful climate for you is a temperate, but slightly cold, one.

YOUR GUIDE TO DIET

To maintain good health, the Virgo native has to exercise caution in selecting the food he eats. Most Virgo-born persons are aware of this, some to the point of becoming what is known as "a health nut." Still, your delicate digestive system and your well-being are at stake, so it is

81

better to be called a health nut or a food faddist than to eat and drink indiscriminately and be ill.

You can easily become *too* preoccupied with the problem of diet, of course, and follows a regimen that does not provide a balanced fare of essential nutrients necessary for the proper functioning of your body.

The rule to follow is simply to avoid those foods and beverages which require a hardy digestion or tend to irritate the intestinal wall because of roughage.

Aside from that, you can and should enjoy a wide variety of meats, fruits, and vegetables. You should place the greatest emphasis, however, on protein foods which can be quickly digested and which provide increased metabolism with its resulting production of energy. A high-protein breakfast is desirable, and might well include a lean ground beef pattie and cottage cheese. English tea is preferable to coffee as a morning beverage.

The worst way for you to start the day is with a breakfast high in carbohydrates, which your system finds difficult to assimilate. Unfortunately, this is the type of breakfast most common in America, usually consisting of orange juice, bacon, potatoes, toast, jelly, and coffee—often drunk with both cream and sugar.

The cell-salt of Virgo is potassium sulphate, which regulates the supply and distribution of oils in the body, and aids in carrying oxygen to cells of the skin.

A deficiency of this salt results in the oils becoming viscous, causing pores in the skin to become clogged. As a consequence, you may experience skin disorders such as acne, eczema, and dandruff.

Foods providing a good source of potassium sulphate are chicory, endive, whole wheat, oats, rye, cheese, almonds, and lean beef.

Yogurt is very beneficial to Virgo natives because it promotes the growth of desirable intestinal bacteria. It also provides the body with predigested protein and B vitamins.

Other foods which meet your nutritional requirements

82

and should be included in your diet are spinach; summer squash; zucchini; celery, okra; citrus fruits; plums; apples; peaches; dates; almonds and walnuts, both well-chewed.

The herbs associated with your sign are rosemary, poke root, summer savory, and valerian. Some of these are used as seasoning in food, some brewed as tea or taken in tablet form as an herbal remedy (sold at health food stores, which are still in business, despite harassment and persecution by the federal Food and Drug Agency, in cooperation with the orthodox medical establishment and with the backing of big food processors).

For you, the key to good health is not just the careful selection of what you eat, but also your state of mind when you eat it. Unless you relax at the table, your digestion and assimilation of meals will be poor.

BREATHING EXERCISE FOR VIRGO

Deep-breathing practice for your sign has a twofold aim— to tranquilize the nervous system and to generate vital forces in the abdominal region. Consistently applied, the following *pranayama* will do both.

Time: Between 2 and 4 p.m.
Place: Garden, patio, or well-ventilated room.
Duration: 3 to 5 minutes.
Technique: Standing or sitting erect, place your right hand, palm downward, upon your solar plexis. It is preferable to do this against the bare skin, rather than to have a layer of clothing between your hand and abdomen.

Now, place your open left hand upon the back of your right one. With eyes closed, inhale slowly through both nostrils to the count of seven. Hold for one count. Exhale seven. Repeat this cycle 16 times, gradually filling your lungs to capacity, but not to the point of discomfort.

♎ LIBRA
The Balance

(September 23 through October 22)

Planetary Ruler: Venus (♀)
Related to: Kidneys, loins, and lumbar region.
Your Body Needs: Foods containing sodium phosphate.
You Should Develop: Self-confidence and ability to face facts.
You Should Avoid: Heavy smoking, hard liquor, indecision, and jealousy.

Libra, the seventh sign of the zodiac, is classified as a Cardinal, airy, positive, nervous sign. Its symbol—the Scales or Balance—correctly identifies its character and influence: In the objective world it brings harmony, equipoise, and symmetry. Esoterically, it governs the relation between the macrocosm and the microcosm, the Self and the Not-self; the neumenon and the phenomenon.

As a Libran, then, you were, so to speak, born at the crossroads of being. For that reason, it is sometimes difficult for you to decide which direction you want to take. You hesitate and weigh and consider. You seek to resolve your dilemma through association and partnership with others. But if these human alliances prove discordant, your health suffers. Disillusionment, even though it stems from your overactive imagination, can result in despondency that can deepen into neurosis or adversely affect the kidneys—the most vulnerable point in your physical make-up.

At such times of stress, for relief you may be tempted to form a dependency upon drugs or alcohol (even though you have no natural tendency toward addiction). Such measures will only complicate your problem by adding ill health. The physical influence of your sign works to keep a chemical and hormonal balance in the body by means of proper secretion and excretion. Poisons in the blood are filtered and carried off as waste in the urine.

You can appreciate the delicate complexity of the kidneys when you realize that each of them contains about 1,200,000 infinitely tiny tubes, the total length of which, in an average adult man, is some 75 miles. The body's blood supply is continuously passing through the kidneys. The fluid to be excreted as urine is collected in a microscopic cup at the end of each tubule.

Prolonged emotional disturbances place an added work load on the kidneys in the form of toxins generated by psychological events. So, if the driving force of your personality keeps tipping the scales of your Sun sign first to one side, then to the other, it might be best for you to seek competent professional help to restore equilibrium to your mind and, in consequence, harmony to your body.

As a rule, the Libran enjoys good health, even though he may not present a robust appearance. The desire for the golden mean, inherent in his nature, usually leads him to impose self-discipline in time to avoid a serious breakdown.

The onset of any illness usually manifests itself by certain symptoms that are typical of your sign. These are acute kidney and bladder disturbances, skin eruptions, or severe headaches. If these conditions persist longer than a few days, you should consult a physician.

Experienced medical astrologers agree that Venus endows her children with a larger than average "sweet tooth"; consequently, you could be tempted to overindulge in rich confections and pastries. If this is true in your case, it would be a good idea to have periodic tests for diabetes, since that is one of the diseases to which the Libra native may be prone. Third-decan Librans (born between September 14 and September 23) in particular should guard against gourmandizing.

The most effective therapy for almost all Libran complaints is complete rest and relaxation in peaceful, harmonious surroundings attended by affectionate, sympathetic friends. You respond to the healing vibrations of music and should experiment with various compositions to determine which have the strongest meditative, relaxing effect on you. For you, there is also great restorative power in the beauty of flowers, great works of art, and quiet conversations with persons possessing a spiritual or artistic nature.

The principal ills to which planetary afflictions in your Sun sign may predispose you are lumbago, anuria, bladder troubles, ulcers, renal calculi, uremia, Bright's disease, diabetes, and (in women) ovarian cysts.

That sounds like a frightening prospect, but bear in mind that the list represents a number of afflicting planetary configurations, most or all of which may not appear in your natal chart at all. For specific indications, consult an astrologer familiar with medical astrology.

YOUR LIBRAN INDIVIDUALITY

It was J. Alfred Prufrock, the subject of T. S. Eliot's famous poem, who asked the question buried deep in every Libran consciousness:

"Do I dare/ Disturb the universe?/ In a minute there is time/ For decisions and revisions which a minute will reverse."

Generally speaking, Libra people favor equipoise. They prefer to strike a balance, to avoid what is known in our troubled times as a confrontation.

This inherent desire for harmony, admirable in moderation, can become the basis for paralyzing indecision. Uncertainty, in turn, can menace your health by building up emotional pressure which will adversely affect the function of your kidneys and bladder.

Paradoxically, while you are a born peacemaker and are greatly upset by strife and discord, you are the perfect Devil's advocate in any discussion. A master of the yes—but, you have the ability to see all sides of any issue, but almost always take the opposition side for the sake of argument. You may "go on about it" for hours, or until your opponent in the debate is worn out and ready to throw in the sponge.

Unconsciously, you seek the approval and admiration of those around you and may often be tempted to do what you think would please others rather than what you would do if you made your decisions on a more objective basis.

Librans born when the Sun is above the horizon and well-aspected possess a keen awareness of what others are thinking and feeling. This faculty, combined with their innate desire for unity with others, gives them the ability to influence people. They speak at exactly the moment their hearers are in a receptive mood.

In affairs of the heart, you are gentle, somewhat withdrawn, and subtle. The less-evolved type in this sign is often flirtatious and philandering. However, all Libra people regard marriage seriously—at first. Realizing perhaps unconsciously, their need for companionship and quiet home surroundings, they choose a mate with care. Unfortunately, there is no statistical proof that their choices are any wiser than those of other Sun signs. On the contrary, too much deliberation can lead to what has been called a marriage of convenience, which may involve years of "quiet desperation" before it ends in eventual divorce.

Librans who respond to the negative influences of their sign sometimes have an overweening self-confidence which leads them to try to plan and direct the lives of their associates. They then become meddlers and interfere with, rather than assist, their friends.

Your inborn tact, sense of justice, and even disposition qualify you for vocations such as diplomat, mediator, judge, or marriage counselor. Librans also enjoy successful careers as artists and art teachers, musicians, interior decorators, sales persons, cosmeticians, social workers, and actors.

Your refined, esthetic tastes make you avoid messy chores and jobs involving untidy surroundings.

You will find Aquarius, Gemini, Leo, and Sagittarius natives most harmonious to your Sun.

THE LIBRAN DIET

In your daily dietary regimen, you will have to guard against the natural tendency of Librans to indulge in what are commonly known as gourmet foods—that is, in dishes which require exotic seasonings and rich sauces; and desserts that consist of ambrosial sweets or French pastries.

The safest course is to plan your regular meals around simple, wholesome foods that will provide the essential nutrients and vitamins your body needs, and to save the epicurean recipes for occasions when you entertain friends.

It is important for Libra people to dine amid pleasant and peaceful surroundings—if possible, with congenial table companions. In a family which includes natives of basically inharmonious signs, this is not always possible, of course; but, if such a condition exists, you can do a great deal to overcome it by learning to withdraw mentally from the center of friction. Soothing "mood" music playing softly in the background can often help you to relax and to soar above the petty or irritating conversation going on around you.

The cell-salt of Libra is sodium phosphate, which helps maintain an acid-alkaline balance in your body, and facilitates the elimination of wastes. If your natal Sun is afflicted, you may from time to time experience a deficiency of this vital element.

You can make certain you are getting the full amount of sodium phosphate your body needs by including the following foods in your daily diet: carrots, asparagus, beets, yellow corn, brown rice, figs, apples, strawberries, peaches, blueberries, almonds, and raisins.

Libran herbs are thyme, watercress, violet, and sorrel.

As a general rule, afflictions to your planetary ruler can be countered effectively by supplementing your diet with additional vitamins A and E; iodine; and the mineral of your sign, which is copper.

Vitamin E is especially important because it is an excellent detoxifying agent, helping the liver to maintain its normal function. It also plays a vital role in treatment of skin disorders and venous troubles such as hemorrhoids and varicose veins. Nutrition studies have shown that vitamin E aids in regulating the menstrual cycle in women and in preventing sterility in both men and women. Natural sources of this vitamin are wheat germ, soybean oil, malt, and alfalfa.

Iodine is necessary for the proper functioning of the thyroid gland, whose hormone—thyroxin—influences the body's basal metabolism. An adequate supply of iodine can be found in seafood, ocean kelp (sold in tablet form at health food stores), radishes, and squash.

The Libran's daily intake of copper should also be given attention. It aids in the production of red blood cells and in the formation of enzymes necessary for proper functioning of the nervous system. Foods that supply copper in the diet are radishes, oysters, cucumbers, and lettuce.

YOGA FOR LIBRANS

Breath control, combined with a stretching exercise, is an

excellent natural way to oxidize the blood and to overcome sluggish circulation.

The following yogic technique should be practiced with the body in a more or less relaxed condition; that is, you should not tense your muscles or fill your lungs beyond their capacity so that a feeling of tightness and suffocation results.

Time: Before 9 a.m. and after 5 p.m.

Place: Well-ventilated room or secluded place in open air.

Duration: 3 to 5 minutes.

Technique: Standing erect (or seated cross-legged in the yogic posture known as *siddhasana* if you have been instructed in yoga) throw your head back and raise your eyes upward toward the ceiling or the sky. Extend your arms outward, level with your shoulders, then raise them above your head, and clasp your hands, interlocking the fingers. In this posture take a deep breath, hold it, and slowly bend the torso from side to side several times, as far as possible without discomfort. The body should bend at the waistline. Drop your arms and exhale, forcing the breath out quickly by drawing in the abdominal muscles. Repeat this exercise ten times.

♏ SCORPIO
The Scorpion or the Eagle

(October 23 through November 21)

Planetary Ruler: Mars (♂); Pluto.
Related to: Generative organs, prostate gland, bladder, rectum.
Your Body Needs: Foods containing calcium sulphate.
You Should Develop: A spirit of forgiveness; better social adjustment.
You Should Avoid: Revengefulness, secrecy, jealousy, and excesses.

If you were born during the period of the year when the Sun was passing through that part of the zodiac symbolized by Scorpio, you have been the victim of a great deal of astrological libel.

Among the ancients, Vettius Valens more or less set the tone that has prevailed ever since in characterizing Scorpio. Scorpio-born persons, he wrote, "are wily, wicked, rapacious, murderers, traitors, unchangeable, a cause of loss, secret plotters, thieves, perjurers, coveters of the goods of others, accessories to murders or poisonings or evil deeds, and haters of their own family."

What was the reason for this absurd and wholly unjustified indictment of an entire Sun sign, and for others like it?

The most likely explanation is that Scorpio is the eighth

sign of the zodiac, corresponding to the Eighth House, which is concerned with sex, death, and the supernatural —all matters that inspire awe and misgivings in most people.

The discovery, in 1930, of the planet Pluto, which is believed to be the octave expression of Mars (Scorpio's traditional ruler) did not help matters.

Leading astrologers agreed that Pluto, described as a "triple-strength Mars," ruled gangsters and the criminal underworld.

Worse, it governed the atom bombs, and it was the active principle in the process of annihilation, both individual and universal. To the long-established fear and foreboding that surrounded the sign were added the horrors of nuclear holocaust on a massive scale.

Had the positive qualities of the sign and its planetary rulers been given equal emphasis with the negative, a wholly different picture might have emerged.

It cannot be denied that the powerful driving force in the life of the Scorpio native is essentially a psychosexual energy, but it is a dynamism that can manifest on the highest levels of intellect and spirituality.

As Thierens correctly observes, Scorpio people are "open to generative and *re*generative as well as to *de*generative influences." The nature of their response depends upon how they use the potential of their libido.

The Hindus, who identify the sex dynamism with that mysterious psychic current called *kundalini,* coiled at the base of the spine, warn that, if it is not controlled, it may rush downward, bringing union with a lower order of creation. Then the carnal appetites are intensified, and lust, perversion, and secret vices take over.

But when the same mystic life force is directed upward through the subtle centers of consciousness that in India are called *chakras,* the native attains illumination. He possesses the spiritual power to transform the world.

It is no doubt because of this diversity of expression the Scorpio is the only sign in the zodiac which has three distinct types—the scorpion, the eagle, and the serpent (sometimes depicted as a lizard).

The afflicted or less-evolved Scorpio person responds to the lower influences of the sign, associated with the scorpion symbol; he is secretive, spiteful, poisonous, hiding in the shadows. But those who seek expression through the higher mind become the eagle, soaring to the heights of spirituality and human achievement.

Illnesses in early adulthood are often the result of maladjustments or unhappiness in childhood. Such emotional traumas seem especially to incline those born under this sign to nervous disorders that sometimes approach hysteria.

Generally speaking, the Scorpio influence seems to have an affinity for infectious and contagious diseases. This is especially true with regard to germs which invade the body through the nose and throat, and those that attack the genitals, urinary tract, and excretory system. During the outbreak of any kind of epidemic, the Scorpio-born would do well to seek isolation until the possibility of contagion is past.

The principal danger areas for you to watch are the reproductive organs, lower bowels, appendix, uretha, coccyx, and sacral plexus.

Some authorities say that, during the early period of the body's evolution, Scorpio's opposite sign—Taurus—took over the rulership of the throat and larynx from Scorpio. It is for that reason that sexual activity is always reflected in the throat and voice. It also means that you must protect yourself against chronic sore throat, especially if afflictions of the Taurus–Leo–Scorpio–Aquarius complex are shown in your birth chart.

Other diseases which are said to affect those of your sign are hepatitis, bladder disorders, and petit mal. Scorpio men often fall victim to prostrate troubles, inguinal hernia, injuries to the sex organs, varicocele, gonorrhea, and syphilis. Women are prone to menstrual irregularities (if the Moon is badly aspected).

93

In the treatment of any illness, Scorpio-people recuperate faster if they are not fussed over or constantly called upon to discuss the state of their health. Left to themselves, they can draw upon an amazing secret reserve of energy and make a prompt recovery. But absolute rest and a hopeful, optimistic outlook are essential.

YOUR INDIVIDUALITY STRUCTURE

Whatever else your detractors may say of you, Scorpio, they cannot characterize you as superficial (as they so often do of Gemini, albeit erroneously). Whether you are influenced by the lower or the higher vibrations of your sign, you manifest a deep intensity, derived from the hidden side of existence.

You have correctly been called the alchemist of the zodiac, because you work upon your environment and all that is in it, including associates and kin, often effecting a transmutation of baser metals into gold, figuratively speaking. At the same time, under your acid tests, much that has passed for the noble metal is revealed to be a low carat alloy.

You have great strength of will and purpose and, once you undertake a task or project, you are inclined to drive yourself—and others—relentlessly to get it done. But you must overcome the tendency to expect others to conform to your views, and to regard them with hostility or suspicion if they do not exhibit the same enthusiasm and zeal that you do in moving toward a chosen goal.

You would be the first to agree with Socrates that the unexamined life is not worth living. Unlike Virgo, who has a keen eye for the faults of others, but is often blind to his own, you start with yourself. Having subjected your innermost feelings and character to the most ruthless scrutiny, you have a realistic idea of your own worth. Because of this, you are usually impervious to both flattery and criticism.

While you like to probe deeply into the personal lives of those in your immediate circle, and to lay bare their most intimate secrets, you go to extremes in guarding your own privacy. Recently, I heard a Los Angeles astrologer say that she always had difficulty in erecting a progressed horoscope or rectifying a natal chart for Scorpio clients because they were so reluctant to disclose any kind of personal information about themselves.

As a parent, you are just, but often severe. Still, your children love you, even if their affection is tempered somewhat with awe. In dealing with them, as will all members of your family and with close friends, you should strive to be a little more demonstrative with your love.

Your health may suffer from your tendency to be self-repressive and to keep your problems to yourself, in preference to discussing them with friends. You must make a real effort to confide in those who love you and who want to help you. Learn to trust them.

In affairs of the heart you are passionate and loyal, but inclined to be too possessive. This attitude leads to jealousies that can undermine what otherwise would be a happy relationship and a harmonious home. It can also lead to the development of one of Scorpio's worst faults—the thirst for revenge. The psychic toxins released into your blood by suspicion and vindictiveness will inevitably take their toll on your general health, as well as on your emotional life.

It is a cliché in astrology tests that Scorpios are intensely loyal friends, but dangerous enemies, for even the higher types are not overburdened with a sense of compassion. The less evolved, negative representatives of the sign are pitiless and often capable of deliberate cruelty. They want not only redress for an injury—imagined or real—but to see their enemies suffer or die. Nor will they hesitate to use any means, fair or foul, to accomplish that end.

At one time or another in your life, you will probably delve into some phase of occultism; Scorpio has an innate

95

curiosity about the unknown and about the profound mysteries of life and death.

Your many natural endowments make it possible for you to achieve success in a wide range of occupations. If you have the typical Scorpio's cool detachment where human suffering is concerned, you can become a skillful surgeon. Your natural ability to ferret out concealed facts and to penetrate other people's secrets could qualify you as a crime reporter for a newspaper, or as an undercover agent.

Scorpios also find rewarding careers as gynecologists, undertakers, laboratory technicians, soldiers, novelists; musicians, composers, and conductors; bank tellers and insurance executives.

Look for assistance needed to carry out your plans from persons whose Sun sign is Gemini. As a rule, you will find that people whose natal Moon was in Scorpio are congenial companions. Natives of Cancer, Virgo, Capricorn, and Pisces are also likely to be harmonious, unless individual planetary configurations indicate otherwise.

SCORPIO GUIDE TO DIET

The Scorpio-born are usually fond of epicurean delights, but are not very skillful in their preparation unless Venus is prominent in their natal charts.

A word of caution is necessary here. Since natives of your sign more often than not have blood with high lipid levels, you should avoid a diet that is too rich in fats. Medical researchers still have much to learn about the body's utilization of cholesterol (a fatty acid), but many scientific studies have provided a sound basis for belief that it helps lay the groundwork for heart attacks.

In any case, a fairly low-fat diet is beneficial to you in that it will help you to keep your weight down, something Scorpios often find difficult in their mature years. Saturated fats (those hard at room temperature, mostly of animal origin) are the chief offenders. By trimming the fat from around your steaks, and reducing the amount of butter, cream, and pastries consumed at each meal, you will go a long way toward striking the desired balance.

A certain amount of essential fatty acids is required to promote the production of bile and for the body to function properly, so that a too severely restricted diet is not wise, either. Paradoxically, eating too little fat can cause you to put on weight, not take it off. A general rule to follow (unless you have had specific advice to the contrary from a competent nutritionist or medical authority) is this: Reduce the amount of animal fats normally present in the American table, and supplement your diet with two tablespoonfuls of unsaturated vegetable oils daily, to provide linoleic acid.

Your high-protein diet should include, besides lean meat: seafood, fowl, eggs, yogurt, nuts, and soybeans.

The cell-salt of Scorpio is calcium sulphate. This element is necessary for rebuilding epithelial tissue and maintaining the body's natural resistance to disease by preventing the accumulation of organic wastes.

Often, the first signs that your body is lacking in this essential will be the onset of nasal congestion, sinusitis, and respiratory infections. A serious deficiency can result in boils, pleurisy, kidney disorders, and liver complaints.

To provide a more adequate amount of calcium sulphate, you must look to fresh fruits and vegetables, since the commercial form of the salt cannot be absorbed by your system.

The principal natural sources of this element are: onions, asparagus, kale, garlic, watercress, mustard greens, cauliflower, leeks, radishes, figs, black cherries, prunes, gooseberries, and coconut.

Herbs which pertain to Scorpio and which provide nutrients and remedies needed by natives of that zodiacal sign are basil, horehound, nettles (drunk as an herb tea), butterbar, and wormwood.

97

Scorpios should supplement their regular dietary regimen with vitamin C, B-complex, and E.

The mineral corresponding to your sign is iron, and the homeopathic remedy is Pulsatilla.

When troubled by constipation, the prudent Scorpio will avoid using the widely advertised laxatives sold in drugstores. These may be irritating and injurious and, at best, give only symptomatic relief. A better way to attack the problem is through diet: more protein, a daily cup of yogurt, or a teaspoonful or two of blackstrap molasses.

YOGIC BREATHING

The theory behind most of the greatly simplified breathing techniques given in these pages is that they not only stimulate or retard certain bodily functions, as required, but that they cleanse the body of many of its impurities by increasing the oxygenation of the blood.

The following exercise is aimed primarily at helping control Scorpio's overabundant sexual energy.

Time: 8 A.M. and 4 P.M.

Place: Well-ventilated room where there are no draughts.

Duration of practice: 5 minutes, morning and evening.

Technique: Seated in an erect posture, close the eyes and breathe slowly and rhythmically in and out, as you allow your body and mind to relax fully. After about two minutes of deep breathing, inhale to the slow count of two; hold the breath for the count of eight, meanwhile gently moving the anal sphincter in and out; then exhale to the count of four through the left nostril if you are male and through the right nostril if you are female. Repeat the full cycle ten times.

After seven weeks of practice, the respective units of time may be lengthened, but they should not exceed 4: 16: 8.

Many teachers of yoga say that the process of sublimating the psychosexual energy will be helped by mentally visualizing an etheric current rising from the base of the spine and passing upward to the brain, while contracting and expanding the sphincter muscles.

↗ SAGITTARIUS
The Archer

(November 22 through December 21)

Planetary Ruler: Jupiter (♃)
Related to: Hips, thighs, coccygeal vertebrae.
Your Body Needs: Foods containing silica.
You Should Develop: Tact, self-discipline, and perseverance.
You Should Avoid: Cigarette smoking, nervous shock, careless driving.

During the zodiacal period in which you were born, the Earth becomes for a time a fellow traveler with the Sun, then overtakes that great luminary and spins on ahead of it until, on December 23, we reach the most distant point from the gravitational center of our galaxy.

It is not too fanciful to say that Sagittarians reflect this cosmic activity in their character and outlook. Throughout their lives, they seem to be outward bound, even against the pull of gravity; and their theme song could well be "Faraway Places."

The Archer (who is also the Centaur) is a far-ranging hunter and explorer, whether on the seas, through tropical jungles, or amid the perilous stone canyons of our cities. The feeling that he is shackled by circumstances or tied down by emotional attachment reacts sooner or later on his health picture. The different forms of nervous disability and the circulatory disorders which afflict natives of this sign very often have a psychogenic origin.

As a Sagittarian, you must guard against an inherent desire for speed and adventure which, in our age, can mean merely a penchant for reckless driving or daredevil sport. You are by nature accident-prone, and such impulsive tendencies can prove calamitous to you.

When injuries occur, they usually involve the pelvis, legs, sacral bones, buttocks, and muscles of the hips and thighs. With advancing years, there may be an increasing risk of falls, so it would be prudent to avoid wet or icy pavements, steep stairs, etc.

Your personal relationship with your physician is an important factor in determining how effectively he can treat you. You have to feel that his interest in your case goes beyond bare clinical considerations of disease, to include the whole man (or woman). And, of course, you are right. The best physician or healer for you would probably be found among the Libra- or Aquarius-born, provided the planetary aspects of his chart are not inimical to yours.

As a child of Jupiter, your optimism and open nature and your willingness to cooperate with the doctor, provided you have confidence in him *and* his medicine, make you a good patient, and you are easily cured. However, you are very suggestible where your state of health is concerned, and should not be exposed to negative persons or ideas while ill.

Generally speaking, the Archer enjoys good health most if not all of his life, unless he consistently undermines it by dictary indiscretions, overindulgence in alcohol, or overexertion. The complaints he does have commonly originate in the liver, the arterial system, or with nervous strain.

Your Sun sign is one of what astrologers call the Mutable Cross, the other three being Gemini, Virgo, and Pisces. Planetary afflictions in your birth chart, to any of these related signs, tend also to influence you. This is especially true of Gemini, your opposite sign. By reflex action, a pathogenic aspect in Sagittarius may result in pulmonary troubles, bronchitis, and other ailments related to Gemini.

If your planetary ruler is badly aspected in your birth map, the production of the Jupiter hormone—insulin—may be interfered with, particularly when the malefic responsible for the mischief is Saturn, the planet of obstruction and atrophy. Insulin controls the sugar in the system, storing it as glycogen when there is an excess supply, and helping to convert it when it is required for energy.

An adversely affected Jupiter should alert you to exercise care in the amount of sugar and fats you consume.

When afflicted, Sagittarius is also associated with the following pathological conditions: sciatica, rheumatism in hips and thighs, enteric disorders, fistula, respiratory troubles, fatty degeneration of the liver, and locomotor ataxia.

THE ARCHER'S PERSONALITY PROFILE

You are by nature straightforward, optimistic, daring, and altruistic—all positive qualities which indicate a friend of mankind.

At the same time, yours is a bicorporeal sign (double-bodied, double-natured), and there is evident at times a paradoxical tendency to be cautious rather than reckless, sensitive and withdrawn rather than extrovertive, reserved rather than outspoken.

Such brief periods, however, are the exception, not the rule. On the whole, your character is stamped with the outgoing, expansive qualities of your planetary ruler, Jupiter. Yours is the urge to explore, to gather experience, to lay new foundations—whether for knowledge, for faith, or for political empires.

It is no accident that Spain, a Sagittarian nation, became the mother of the Conquest in the fifteenth and sixteenth centuries. It was under her flags that Columbus and his contemporaries made their epic voyage of discovery. Balboa, discoverer of the Pacific Ocean, carried the standard of the Virgin and Castile upheld in his right hand as he strode back and forth in the surf, his naked sword upraised in his left, ranting the proclamation by which he took possession "now and for all time, so long as the world shall last and until the final universal judgment of all mankind."

The high spirits which course through the Archer never seem to subside completely. At flood tide, they sometimes inspire him with the kind of megalomania Sagittarian Mark Twain described:

"When I'm playful," he wrote, "I use the meridians of longitude and parallels of latitude for a seine, and drag the Atlantic ocean for whales. I scratch my head with the lightning and purr myself to sleep with the thunder."

If you are not careful, this overweening confidence and optimism can lead you into unsound or risky ventures, which promise rich rewards, but turn out to be "blue-sky" promotions.

You are extremely proud of your lineage and of your friends, home, country, and talents, and you feel humiliated and distressed at the slightest hint that they may not be all you sincerely believe them to be.

In other words, you create your own world and expect others to see in it what you see. Yet the truth is that, as the esoterist has pointed out, the Sagittarian "carries his own light and looks at the world in the lustre it spreads."

Cruelty of any kind is foreign to your nature, and you will go to great lengths to avoid hurting others. Ironically, your direct approach to everything, including human relationships, often results in tactless remarks which, while wholly unintentional, deeply offend intimates and strangers alike.

Marriage for the Sagittarian can be and often is an unhappy experience, unless he finds a mate who understands his deep-felt need for personal freedom and is prepared to go along with it. You want to feel that your marriage partner has the utmost faith in you; and you cannot bear any kind of domestic strife, jealousy, or restrictions very long.

The cause of your increasing irritability and restlessness in such circumstances may not be apparent to your intimates because you try to avoid whenever possible the unpleasantness of a family row. Your solution may be simply to "walk out," often to some distant place.

I knew an instance of the kind, involving a Sagittarian girl married to a Gemini man. (Unions between these two signs are surprisingly common even though they impose formidable problems of mutual adjustment.) In the case I have just cited, the Sagittarian wife felt that Mr. Gemini, who was far from being a homebody himself, expected her to spend too much time in the nest. There were no arguments or protests; but, returning home from a two-day business trip, the Twin was astounded and heartbroken (until anger took over) to find that his spouse had packed up and left. A brief note on the mantelpiece explained that she had taken this course so they would not hurt each other in a bitter quarrel.

You are attracted to profound subjects such as philosophy, ethics, and religion; and you frequently associate yourself with progressive causes. While you normally balance a flexible and ingenious mind with your keenly felt emotions, you can be stirred to high indignation and passionate action by injustice.

Such outbursts take a great toll on your breath, and you would be wise to avoid them whenever possible. You are simply not the stellar type to become "involved," in the present-day meaning of that word. As a political activist, you soon become tense and irritable and make hasty judgments that you later regret. This is particularly the case with second decanate Sagittarians (December 2 to December 11) who come under the dominating influence of Mars.

With your friends and with the world at large, you enjoy

104

an easy-going, open-hearted relationship. Unlike Scorpio, you believe in putting all your cards on the table, and anything devious or underhanded is repugnant to you.

In your personal life, you are freer of sexual hang-ups and perversions than almost any other signs of the zodiac. This does not mean that your sex drive is not strong. It is. Moreover, being a born hunter, you thoroughly enjoy the chase, if you are male, and the strategy, if you are a female Archer. Both are considerate and satisfying lovers.

If you will overcome your innate desire always to seek greener pastures, you can forge a successful career in any vocation requiring a versatile, intuitive mind; the ability to teach and demonstrate; a talent for promotion and publicity; and an impartial, judicial faculty.

Possessing these qualities, it is not surprising that Sagittarians often become lawyers, bankers, teachers, clergymen, publishers, advertising executives, public relations men, travel agents, athletic coaches, prospectors, and recreation directors.

Negative traits to be watched: a tendency to leave one job or task unfinished to go on to something else, sarcasm, gambling, and irresponsibility.

GUIDE TO NUTRITION

The principal rule that should govern the Sagittarian dietary regimen is: Exercise restraint in the consumption of rich foods and condiments. Jupiter influences the liver and the arterial system and, when adversely aspected, tends to disturb the function of these vital parts of the body. Exotic dishes and gourmet desserts, which have an almost irresistible appeal to the typical Archer's palate, give the bloodstream an excess of acid-forming elements, including the fatty acid, cholesterol, which may become embedded in the arterial walls, with the result that circulation to the legs and feet is restricted. Leg cramps then occur, sometimes so severe that they prevent sleep.

105

Similarly, occlusion of coronary arteries feeding the heart, or of blood vessels in the brain, may cause heart attacks and strokes, especially in later years.

In order to insure that your liver is performing the scores of tasks assigned to it, you must make certain that it is adequately supplied with several nutrients, the most important of which are vitamin C and the B-complex vitamins.

One of the B vitamins, cholin, plays an especially vital role in maintaining good health. It is needed to assist the body in utilizing fats. Research studies have shown that a severe deficiency of cholin causes degenerative changes in and death of liver cells. Cholin is found in wheat germs, calf's liver, egg yolks, and soybean lecithin. It is also available in tablet form in many health food stores.

Your liver also needs a consistent, ample supply of vitamin C to combat chemical poisons that find their way into the blood stream from a number of sources, including food which has been treated with toxic additives.

Vitamin C (ascorbic acid) will help prevent the breakdown of capillary veins.

The cell-salt of Sagittarius is silica, occurring naturally in crystallized form as common quartz.

The pancreas contains a substantial amount of silica, and normal muscle tissue requires it. The salt is also present in the bones, the connective tissue of the brain, and in the sheaths covering the nerves. It is a good insulator, and helps retain its heat during cold weather.

Silica also causes disintegrating matter, such as pus from boils and pimples, to rise to the surface of the skin, and acts as a healing agent at the place of eruption.

You may well suspect a deficiency in your zodiacal cell-salt if your hair lacks a healthy luster, your fingernails are weak and brittle, your eyelids inflamed and your gums sore or abcessed.

Dietary sources of assimilable silica are the edible skins of fruits and vegetables, figs, strawberries, prunes, Scotch oats, parsnips, unpolished rice, and ripe cherries.

It is also found in typically Sagittarian herbs such as marjoram, mallows, agrimony, and sage.

YOGIC BREATHING

In India, most, if not all, yogic breathing exercises include some kind of autosuggestion along with the control of *prana* or the "vital air." Many teachers of yoga regard autosuggestion itself as a form of energy, which is directed by will and visualization to any desired part of the body. Charged with an electromagnetic force, it can heal any mental or physical disorder, provided it is applied consistently over the period of time necessary to make it work.

The following technique involves breath control, autosuggestion, and mental repetition of a vibratory syllable, called a *mantram*.

Time: 8 to 9 A.M. and 4 to 5 P.M.

Place: Secluded place outdoors, if possible. Otherwise, a well-ventilated room.

Duration of practice: 5 minutes.

Technique: Seated comfortably in a straight chair, close your eyes and relax for a moment, passively allowing the vibrations of nature around you to penetrate your body and mind.

Slowly and deeply inhale, counting to seven. Allow one time unit to reverse the breath flow, then slowly exhale while you again count to seven. Assist your lungs in the expulsion of air by drawing in the abdominal muscles. Repeat the in-and-out cycle ten times.

Now place the open palm of your right hand over your liver. (It is located in the upper right area of the abdominal cavity, immediately below the diaphragm.) Once again, breathe slowly and rhythmically in and out. But instead of counting, mentally repeat the syllable *hromm,* drawing it out to the equivalent of seven time units. Meanwhile, visualize a current of energy passing down your arm and into the liver. Repeat the cycle ten times.

♑ CAPRICORN
The Sea Goat

(December 22 to January 20)

Planetary Ruler: Saturn (♄)
Related to: Knees, skeleton, skin, and (by reflex action) the digestive system.
Your Body Needs: Foods containing calcium phosphate.
You Should Develop: An optimistic outlook and greater freedom of expression.
You Should Avoid: Selfishness and melancholy.

It has been said that the natives of Capricorn live life in reverse. They are born old and get younger as the years go by.

While this generalization should not be taken too literally, it is true that, in early childhood, the Capricornian often seems too serious and mature for his age. As he grows older, however, he very gradually loses some of the sobriety that characterized his youth.

Even so, all through life, the typical Goat should strive to overcome the influence of his sign, which frequently hovers about him like an invisible aura that his associates sometimes find very depressing. Strangers, who do not perceive the sterling qualities of character which lie concealed behind his Gloomy Gus exterior, may turn away, thus adding to the Capricornian's tendency to martyrdom. The resulting emotional inhibition (so characteristic of

Saturn's influence) adversely affects the native's general health by aiding the process of crystallization, natural to the sign.

Capricorn is associated with minerals in the body, the outer skin (cuticle or epidermis), the connective tissue, the superficial mucous surfaces and the sympathetic peripheral nerves.

Your sign also governs the knees, the body's bony structure, and the tendons and the cartilage holding it together. That is why the most frequent accidents of Capricorn involve broken bones, bruises, sprains, dislocations, and knee injuries.

From birth until about the seventh year, those of your nativity are rarely very strong; but from that point on, unless there are severe afflictions in their natal charts, their vitality increases, although they will never possess the stamina of the more robust signs of the zodiac.

Nevertheless, you do not readily give in to illness and, if you exercise normal prudence about health matters, you will probably live to an active and healthy old age. Yours is a sign of longevity, despite the fact that the life-giving Sun is weak in Capricorn. Many of you will just be hitting your stride when others of your age group have "had it" and are ready for the rocking chair.

When illness does strike, it tends to become chronic because of the Saturn influences. Capricorn people have a tendency to brood over their ailments (as well as over many other things) and to hold on to them, often becoming hypochondriacs. Their belief that their condition is hopeless becomes a self-fulfilling prophecy.

Your principal health problems are likely to be impeded and irregular function of those organs which come under the rule of Capricorn and Saturn. Circulation of the blood through the tissues may become sluggish; elimination may be restricted, so that toxins and waste matter build up in the body; and there may be a tendency toward a reflex action to the stomach, ruled by the opposite sign, Cancer.

110

The formation of calcium deposits in the bursa, and rheumatism, arthritis, and neuralgia are disorders which fall under your sign.

Capricorn also directly influences the *function* of the gall bladder and, when afflicted, may cause an insufficient flow of bile. When Saturn is in Capricorn in the natal chart, this condition is extremely likely. The late Dr. William Davidson reported that much epithelioma and skin cancer have their roots in this often-overlooked tendency.

YOUR CAPRICORN INDIVIDUALITY

Your sign of Capricorn, ancient as time, has come down to us trailing strange associations from the remote past. Its symbol, the sea-goat represents the higher mind, and has been identified with various mythical god-creatures who emerged from the sea (Jung's collective unconscious) to teach mankind the arts of civilization. After his period of tutelage was over, he always returned to the sea from whence he came.

The goat has also appeared as a symbol in the initiatory rites of secret societies, good and bad, over the centuries. The most familiar figure, of course, is that of Satan, the Prince of Darkness, presiding at the Witches' Sabbath.

The natives of Capricorn are typically somewhat aloof, consciously or unconsciously imposing a barrier between themselves and others. Even when their work brings them into close contact with others, they retain within themselves a secret place of solitude into which the most intimate acquaintance or loved one is never allowed to penetrate.

Billionaire Howard Hughes, who is a first-decan Capricorn, has displayed in the extreme many of the traits traditionally associated with the sign. With advancing years, he withdrew more and more from the world, in which he still had vast and active financial interests, until

111

he became a confirmed recluse, whose privacy is guarded by a corps of ex-policemen, former FBI men, and undercover informants. Thus ensconced behind the ramparts of mystery and silence, he schemes and lays bold plans on a grand scale, enjoying the dream castles of his secluded world with the kind of intensity that one writer has called "the loftiest intoxications of genius."

Capricorn represents big industrial and commercial enterprises which employ a large number of people. You are naturally attracted to this world, and your chances of success in it are very good, owing to your patient, calculating, resourceful nature.

Mining, real estate, banking, and public engineering projects which benefit the community at large are all governed by your planetary ruler, Saturn. You would also find a rewarding career as a politician, actor, playwright, osteopath, or scientist.

One of the keynotes of the Capricornian make-up is perservance; and this trait, coupled with your strong determination to realize your ambitions, enables you to pick your way cautiously to the top.

While all Capricornians are to some extent self-centered, the negative type is selfish, tight-fisted, pessimistic, and narrow in outlook.

Being hypersensitive, you often take offense at things said or done in all innocence by those around you. You should guard against the tendency of those born under your constellation to hold a grudge and to be forgiving. Remember that resentments held over a long period can have neurotic consequences. Ultimately, the psychogenic poisons they create will result in digestive upsets through overacidity.

You have a deep-felt need for love from those close to you, but sometimes alienate them because you find it difficult to be very demonstrative of your own affection. A marriage partner who learns to adjust to your emotional reserve, however, will learn to value your faithful and serious attitude toward the wedded state. But it won't be easy.

As a parent, you are likely to be stern, although just, with your children, and unless planetary aspects give contrary testimony, you will probably enjoy a more carefree, happy relationship with them than with your mate.

Capricorn promises a long life, in spite of the diseases and infirmities to which the sign is heir. Unless adverse planetary aspects act to shorten your lifespan by disease or accident, you can expect to live to an advanced age. A study conducted by the Church of Light in Los Angeles seemed to indicate that Capricorn as a Sun sign offered long life to men more often than to women.

You have a Spartan streak in you, and even if you inherit or amass a fortune, you are often inclined to conserve money rather than to spend it on personal luxuries. Second-decan natives (January 2 to January 11) are sometimes an exception, being under the rulership of Venus.

One of the best auguries for good health in your case is a robust sense of humor—not the wry sort of wit or saturnine waggery at someone else's expense that is so often encountered in natives of your sign—but the ability to see the lighter side of life. Above all, you need to take yourself a little less seriously. First-decan Capricornians, especially, should learn to laugh at themselves and at the world's follies. Moods of anxiety and depression, so detrimental to your health, can be relieved by joining congenial friends for an evening at the theater or a game of cards.

To sum up:

You are industrious, conservative, thrifty, methodical, and cautious. Your life is based firmly upon permanent structures and enduring values, whether they be material, social, or spiritual.

Your primary purpose in life is to build a foundation for communal relationships. Your basic weakness is being indifferent to or oblivious of people as individuals, with widely varying emotional needs and attitudes.

113

CAPRICORN GUIDE TO DIET

The zodiacal Goat, unlike his counterpart in the animal kingdom, cannot eat anything and everything with impunity.

Because of Saturn's influence, which tends to inhibit the function of secretive organs such as the liver and gall bladder, your system is not prepared for assault by highly spiced or greasy foods, gravies, or alcohol. Chocolate and mayonnaise are also undesirable, all the more so if your birth date happens to fall within the first decan of the sign (December 22 to January 1).

While your daily diet should include an adequate proportion of protein foods to offset the innate tendency of your sign toward lowered body temperature and to stimulate production of antibodies, the so-called gourmet cuts of meat, high in fat, are not for you. Instead, you can get the proteins you need from lean meat, yogurt, cottage cheese, eggs, and lentils.

You should drink plenty of water between meals. However, recent scientific studies have provided evidence that the chlorine used in most public water systems destroys Vitamin E, which is essential to your health. To avoid this possibility, you should drink boiled or bottled water.

Medically oriented astrologers all agree that, when Saturn is prominent and afflicted in the birth chart or when there is a progressed aspect involving Saturn, the native falls victim to anxieties and fears which cause an increase in the amount of adrenalin in the blood.

Dr. Cornell observed that, when such a condition exists, the unawakened and drifting Saturnian frets, mopes, and worries, thereby rendering himself liable to severe liver complaints, suicidal mania, and chronic ailments in general.

The late C. C. Zain, who made an extensive study of the pathogenic influences of the planets, noted further that people who are responding to the discordant thought-cell activity triggered by such configurations sometimes fall into a state of anxiety when there is really no serious problem confronting them. "Such chronic anxiety," he writes, "which is fear that some situation is going to appear which they cannot adequately handle, causes a constant drain upon the adrenalin supply."

To combat Saturnine afflictions of this kind, Zain recommended a high-protein diet, supplemented with a variety of mineral salts and vitamins.

The cell-salt of Capricorn is calcium phosphate, which utilizes albumen from the food to help build up and to maintain the body's bony structure. When there is a deficiency of this cell-salt, albumen is not retained and used, but passes out of the body through the kidneys. Among the disorders resulting from such a loss are kidney troubles, rheumatism, and acid indigestion. The unused albumen may also cause skin eruptions and boils. If it accumulates in the ear, it can eventuate in deafness.

Foods that supply the body with calcium phosphate are cabbage, asparagus, spinach, lentils, brown beans, celery, almonds, cucumbers, barley, egg yolk, lean meats, whole wheat, strawberries, figs, blueberries, and plums.

Herbs traditionally associated with your Sun sign and which have both medicinal and nutritional uses are Solomon's seal, red beet, mullein, knotweed, amaranthus, and quince tree.

YOGA FOR CAPRICORN

In the preceding analysis of your Sun sign, one thing stands out as being of prime importance to the Capricorn-born in maintaining mental and physical well-being. It is the need to avoid depression and a negative state of mind. Most ills that commonly strike those of your sign originate with or are assisted by anxiety, even if that anxiety was activated by adverse stellar influences.

115

It follows that many such ailments can be prevented or at least palliated, by transcendence of the self. How can this be accomplished?

Yoga is one means. It is a well-settled postulate in astrology that those whose destinies are related to the celestial pattern marked by Capricorn possess within themselves a kind of spiritual citadel, which Teresa of Avila called "the interior castle."

Even the most hardened materialist (and there are many under this constellation) can learn to close his eyes and to withdraw into this "solitude of the soul."

For those who need a point of focus, the following yogic technique will be useful. Try it at least three times before you pass judgment upon its effectiveness.

Time: 7 to 8 A.M. and 11 P.M. to midnight.

Place: A quiet, well-ventilated room, free of draughts.

Duration of Practice: 10 minutes or longer.

Technique: Seated erect in a straight chair, calm the mind by breathing gently and rhythmically in and out, as you mentally count to time the exercise. Inhale seven, hold one, exhale seven. Repeat the cycle ten times or more.

Now, still seated, rest the elbows on a pillow or a cushion placed before you on a table or desk top. Place your thumbs lightly upon the tragus (small flap) of each ear, thus closing your ears to all exterior sounds. Close your eyes and rest your under fingers lightly over the lids. Press your lips together between the remaining two fingers. Continue breathing normally through the nose. Concentrate your attention solely upon sounds to be heard in the closed ears.

According to teachers of yoga, these sounds vary with the degree of spiritual development. You may hear a humming sound, like a swarm of bees; the sound of a small silver chain; the ringing of bells; the roar of the sea; etc.

After some practice, you will find that your mind is

116

more and more absorbed in these sounds, so that you forget your bodily senses and thought.

Gradually, your mind will remain free for longer periods until your fears and anxieties disappear.

≈ AQUARIUS
The Water-Bearer

(January 21 through February 19)

Planetary Ruler: Uranus (♅)
Related to: Ankles, wrists, bones of lower limbs, eyesight.
Your Body Needs: Food containing sodium chloride.
You Should Develop: Your intuitive powers; concern for the individual.
You Should Avoid: Excessive fatigue; erratic habits; procrastination.

Symbolically, your sign is something of a contradiction. Although it is one of the airy triplicity—which should suggest the mobility of thistledown—it is also fixed, signifying the opposite quality of inertness.

To add to the confusion, the name Aquarius implies a watery correspondence, but, in fact, refers only to the sign's representative figure—a water-bearer who dispenses the water of life to the whole world.

These seeming paradoxes are, to a certain extent, reflected in both your physical make-up and your personality. When well-aspected at birth, your sign gives a beautiful physique, with abundant vitality; but, at the same time, you remain somehow delicate and subject to nervous debility under prolonged stress.

Similarly, your general disposition is often difficult for your friends and family to understand, since you are optimistic in your over-all outlook, but frequently moody and given to spells of seeming indifference and gloom.

Aquarians generally enjoy good health; but there is the ever-present need to purify the blood with the proper dietary regimen, aided by vitamins and minerals.

When illness does come, it is often quite sudden and may be brought on by irregular habits, by tensions you have allowed to build up or that result from suppressed emotions, and by pushing yourself beyond the safe limits of physical endurance.

You are more sensitive than the natives of other signs to the changes in planetary configuration and may experience puzzling psychic disturbances as a consequence. It is important for you to recognize these periods as being transitory and not to allow yourself to be deeply affected by them. Be on your guard against despondency and melancholy, which can undermine your general health.

Aquarians often have a tendency toward varicose veins, swollen ankles, and muscular spasms in the legs. If possible, therefore, you should avoid occupations which require you to spend a great deal of time on your feet.

In the later decades of life, you may develop high blood pressure and hardening of the arteries unless, during your early years, you take measures to prevent these conditions. Aside from following a fairly low-fat diet, one of the easiest and most effective ways to maintain a healthy cardiovascular system is a program of daily exercise in the open air. Generally speaking, Aquarians are not enthusiastic about exercise for health's sake, but it is extremely important in helping you keep fit.

If your natal Sun is adversely aspected by one or more of the malefic planets, during critical periods of your life you may be prone to accidents involving electrical equipment, explosions, improperly administered drugs, and x-ray treatments.

Aquarius people sometimes suffer from strange or uncommon ailments of mysterious origin, which are difficult for orthodox practitioners to diagnose or treat. In such cases, the services of a medical astrologer are invaluable. He will be able to determine, from your natal and progressed charts, the nature of the peculiar condition, as well as the kind of therapy needed to cure it.

Leg cramps are a common complaint of your sign, partly because of poor circulation and partly from want of daily exercise. A number of drugstore remedies have been recommended for relief of this painful affliction, including quinine sulphate capsules (3 to 5 grains). However, a Chicago physician suggests a simpler treatment. He says that breathing in and out of a small paper bag two or three times will relieve the spasm. This should be followed by a massage of the muscle, rubbing only in a downward motion, all the way from knee to heel or to the toes. Repeat the rubdown for two or three successive days.

BASIC AQUARIAN PSYCHOLOGY

Evangeline Adams, who was herself an Aquarian, identified the water-bearer of the sign-symbol as Isis Unveiled: "She pours forth science, progress, nobility of thought and conduct, the wisdom of the stars, giving freely to others, while she herself is refreshed and renewed by that life-giving stream."

Miss Adams was obviously writing of the more highly evolved natives of the sign, since Aquarius, like other arcs of the zodiac, has its negative side as well. Furthermore, in our time, not everything that goes by the designation Aquarian is entitled to that determination.

There is considerable disagreement among astrologers as to exactly when the Aquarian Age dawned or is yet to dawn. According to the late C. C. Zain of the Brotherhood of Light, the Age began January 19, 1881.

Astrologers at the Rosicrucian Fellowship in Oceanside, California, on the other hand, say that the Aquarian Age will not be fully with us for another 600-odd years, or approximately 2,600 A.D.

Regardless of just when we enter the Aquarian Age, those of your sign must be considered the forerunners of the new cosmic cycle.

The stellar pattern at the time of your birth gives a gentle, obliging, and loyal disposition. Even the unawakened natives of the sign will rarely engage in violent acts or be involved in family fights and barroom brawls.

Your outlook on the world is characterized by a philosophical detachment and unconventionality. At the same time, you have a deep intuition which makes you a good judge of character.

Your circle of friends is likely to represent the entire social spectrum, from the wealthy and famous to the indigent and infamous. Having an innate sense of brotherhood, you treat all of them with the same courtesy and somewhat impersonal amiability.

The Aquarian mind is inquisitive and penetrating. There is a tendency to ignore completely the prevailing moral or political opinions of society and to embrace radical ideas with great fervor, as though they were divinely revealed truths. It is very easy for you to become a fanatic, whether it be in the religious sphere, or in politics, science, or art.

Yours is what has been called "the gift of the spirit"— a kind of psychic power which seeks to express itself in broad humanitarian undertakings. Consequently, you experience your greatest sense of fulfillment and happiness in working with organizations and groups dedicated to some program for helping mankind.

Great spiritual healers are born under your sign, and it has been said that every Aquarian is a natural healer, though, oddly enough, few are aware of it. There is no doubt that Aquarian people can exert a strange and calming influence over persons who are emotionally upset. Even mental patients respond to your quieting presence,

Once you have made up your mind to embark upon a

certain course of action, you are capable of great industry and strength of purpose. As an employee or business associate, you are honest and dependable, believing, as you do, in a code of personal honor.

One weakness of your sign against which you should be ever vigilant is that of not keeping promises. Other personality flaws to which Aquarians are prone include: escapism, vacillation, caprice, and pessimism.

Aquarians are likely to have unhappy or emotionally unrewarding marriages, owing partly to the fact that they are not demonstrative in their affection and often are unable to transfer to an individual the same intense love and solicitude they feel for humanity at large.

While it may not be apparent to outsiders, domestic crises and inharmony do take their toll on the hypersensitive Aquarian psyche, often resulting in various psychosomatic ailments. The most common of these are neuralgia, nervous disorders, kidney troubles, and uncommon or obscure illnesses that are difficult to identify.

Aquarius people are very susceptible to mental suggestion, whether it is received from persons close to them, or in the form of hypnosis, given by a hypnotist or self-administered.

This sensitivity can be used to great advantage in the practice of autosuggestion, by means of which you can overcome all psychogenic illnesses, and many that are not.

The best basic text for the beginner in this important art is still the work of the famous French mental healer who first perfected it, Emile Coué. His celebrated general formula (*Tous les jours, a tous points de vue, je vais de mieux en mieux* [Day by day, in every way, I'm getting better and better]) was devised as a kind of preliminary instrument of thought, in some respects similar to the Hindu *mantram,* aimed at gaining access to deeper levels of consciousness. Coué himself observed that such a phrase is easy to repeat: "The youngest child can understand it, and it possesses a rudimentary rhythm, which exerts a lulling effect on the mind, and so aids in calling up the unconsciousness."

Although many persons scoffed at Coué's work, he and his followers accomplished near-miracles in healing at his clinic in Nancy, France.

The fundamental principles of his technique are more urgently needed in our day than in his, now that a whole generation is suffering the ill effects of induced suggestion from that most diabolical of all hypnotists, the television screen, often correctly referred to as the Idiot Eye.

THE AQUARIAN DIET

Unless the planetary pattern of your birth chart indicates otherwise (for example, Venus in Cancer), it is unlikely that food holds a very important place in your life. You can enjoy to the fullest a beautiful table, laden with choice fare; but you will derive as much if not more pleasure from a hearty meal cooked over the campfire in some outdoor retreat.

The ruler of your sign is Uranus, considered by astrologers to be one of the strongest planets, despite its great distance from the Earth. Dr. Cornell was of the opinion that very few persons in our age are as yet sufficiently awakened spiritually to respond to this planet's higher vibrations, and that both Uranus and Neptune will exert a more positive influence on future races of man.

The physical effects of this planet include a tendency to poor circulation, especially in the blood vessels of the kidneys and of the legs. Because of this, the Aquarian diet should be supplemented with vitamin C and bioflavenoids (including rutin) to strengthen the body's venous system. Vitamin E in substantial daily amounts (100 to 300 I.U.) is also helpful in the prevention of vascular troubles, especially after the age of 35.

Fresh fruits, such as oranges, lemons, apples, pears,

grapes, and pineapple, should be represented on your daily menu.

When Uranus is badly aspected, there is a tendency for the parathyroid glands to be affected so that they secrete insufficient hormones to insure a normal calcium-sodium balance. The result is increased nervous tension, irritability, and fatigue.

The calcium reserve must be replenished by eating calcium-rich foods, such as milk, hard cheese, mustard and turnip greens, soybeans, blackstrap molasses, and almonds.

The cell-salt of Aquarius is sodium chloride, familiar to everyone as common table salt. If you have ever left salt exposed in a fairly damp place, you know that it has the property of attracting moisture. In the body, it performs the function of attracting water, which it carries along the intestinal tract and through the tissues. Here we see how opposite is the symbol of your sign—the Water Bearer.

When there is a deficiency of sodium chloride in the body, water—which makes up 70 percent of the human organism—is not properly controlled and distributed. The effect of such an insufficiency may be the development of dropsy, catarrh, diarrhea, and, in extreme cases, delirium.

Unfortunately, you cannot remedy a deficiency of sodium chloride by simply adding more table salt to your diet. Ordinary salt will not enter the bloodstream because it is too coarse to be absorbed by the fine tubules of mucous membrane which normally assimilate such elements. In fact, too much table salt in the food can result in eventual hardening of the arteries, skin disorders, stroke, and kidney troubles.

The proper way to supplement your supply of the Aquarian cell-salt is to eat foods which provide it in an assimilable form which can be extracted by the digestive organs.

Foods which contain significant amounts of sodium

chloride are: cabbage, spinach, asparagus, celery, radishes, carrots, corn, lentils, ocean fish and sea food, strawberries, apples, and figs.

Your cell-salt is supplied in more concentrated form (in case a severe deficiency exists) in the biochemic remedy *Natrum Muriaticum,* which is available in tablet form.

Among the herbs identified with Aquarius are comfrey root, tansy, sea holly, and uva ursi.

The homeopathic remedy of Aquarius is *Arsenicum album.*

BREATHING TECHNIQUE

The basic aims of this exercise are to stimulate circulation, calm the nerves, and increase the flow of magnetic energy throughout the body. It will also aid in maintaining the balanced function of the ductless glands, two of which (the front pituitary and the parathyroid) are especially important to the health of Aquarius people.

Time: 7 to 9 A.M.

Place: Open air, in the shade.

Duration of Practice: Approximately 8 minutes.

Technique: Seated in an erect posture (the *Siddha-asana,* if you know yoga; otherwise in a straight chair) try to make your mind as blank as possible. Gently fill the lungs with air, breathing in for the time required to count to four. Hold the breath for sixteen counts (unless it is uncomfortable, in which case, begin with eight and increase the number after a week or two of practice). Breathe out to the count of eight.

Repeat this cycle 10 times daily during the first month of practice; 15 times the second month; and 20 times the third.

When inhaling, imagine that you are drawing the breath

125

downward to the navel. When exhaling, mentally picture the breath flow extending outward about nine inches from the nose.

♓ PISCES
The Fish

(February 20 through March 20)

Planetary Ruler: Neptune (♆)
Related to: Feet, body's fluids, gastroabdominal region (by reflex); pineal gland; and lymphatic system.
Your Body Needs: Foods containing phosphate of iron.
You Should Develop: Will power; closer contact with reality.
You Should Avoid: Alcohol, opiates, self-indulgence.

Pisces is the final sign of the zodiac, marking the end of the Sun's annual journey around the ecliptic. It is related to the life sphere denoted by the terminal Twelfth House, concerned with the unconscious mind, sorrows, secret aspirations, inner development, seclusion or confinement, selfless acts, and life after death.

In view of such correspondences as these, it is not surprising that most authorities consider Pisces the most spiritual sign of the twelve. It gives us the poet-dreamer, the lyrical writer, the explorer, the musician, and artist.

There is the unevolved, negative side, too. Natives who respond to the lower vibrations of the sign often drift through life, following their will-o'-the-wisp fantasies, gradually sinking lower until death frees them from the chaos of their existence.

As a rule, Pisceans born during the first two decanates

of the sign (February 20 to March 12) do not have abundant physical energy, although their general health is good. Those whose birth dates fall in the third decanate (March 12 to March 20) are stronger because they come under the domination of Mars, the planet of energy.

As a Piscean, your health problems most frequently stem from emotionally induced conditions, rather than from exposure to germs or other factors outside yourself. Even when you appear calm and relaxed you may be quivering with anxiety or quacking with apprehension within. Such states adversely affect the functioning of your endocrine system, thereby laying the groundwork for those ailments to which you are predisposed.

When you do fall ill, you have a tendency to be pessimistic about your chances for an early recovery. Friends and intimates who sympathize with you and encourage you to talk about your complaint only make matters worse, despite their good intentions. By discussing your symptoms, you focus your mind on the idea that you are indeed ill. This idea, passed on to the unconscious mind, is self-fulfilling, so to speak, and without any physical reason for it, the course of your illness takes the downgrade.

According to Dr. William E. Davidson, Pisces is associated not only with the feet, as traditionally noted in astrology texts, but, for some reason not clearly understood, also dominates the duodenum—the widest part of the small intestine which leads immediately out of the stomach.

It appears, said Dr. Davidson, that calcium is absorbed at that point in the gastrointestinal tract, so that when Mars is ill-aspected in the natal chart, the native is likely to have some degree of duodenitis. When such an affliction is present, there is also a calcium deficiency, with the resulting tooth cavities which often require fillings early in life.

Inadequate calcium in the blood also has an adverse effect on the sympathetic nervous system, producing irritability which, in turn, causes the emotional upsets that pose a constant threat to the Pisces person's health.

Generally speaking, the diseases of your sign are often obscure and difficult to diagnose. They require the attention of a doctor who is careful and painstaking in his examination, before he prescribes treatment. A general practitioner—commonly called the "family doctor"—will in most cases be the best physician for you, rather than a specialist.

Piscean afflictions include tumors and fungus growths, mucus in the lungs and intestinal tract, glandular disorders, softening of tissues, tender or swollen feet, and conjunctivitis.

Accidents which most commonly befall natives of this sign involve those areas ruled by Pisces. Thus, you should guard against injury to the feet by wearing the proper shoes, including arch supports, if prescribed by a competent chiropodist. Do not neglect deep cuts and scratches especially if you are a third-decanate Piscean (March 12 to March 20), under the influence of Mars. Serious infections such as tetanus can ensue, if wounds are not treated promptly.

BASIC INDIVIDUALITY FACTORS

The key words of the Piscean individuality are sympathy, inspiration, psychism, self-sacrifice, and indecision.

If different astrological types can be viewed as being basically senders and receivers (and in a broad general sense, they can), you are a receiver. This means, simply, that you are mentally impressionable and emotionally receptive to everything and everyone around you.

Such sensitivity can be a good thing, provided you stay tuned to those people and things which are uplifting and help build character. On the other hand, unless you exercise vigilance, you may be just as easily influenced by persons and conditions of a lower order, much to your detriment. Pisces, remember, is related to the Twelfth House, sometimes called the House of self-undoing.

This position of the Sun at birth makes you intensely aware of the distress and suffering of people, regardless of their social status or relation to you. For these you show the utmost compassion, whether they deserve it or not. Pisces has been stirred to the depths by the world's ills, and can find only one answer to the problem of evil: self-sacrifice, which is motivated partly by a profound sense of pity and partly by a spirit of atonement.

You have an inherent delicacy and refinement, often including an esthetic sense which may find expression through art, music, or literature. When planetary aspects favor the voice, Pisceans become famous as singers. Both Caruso and Geraldine Farrar were natives of your sign. Both achieved greatness because they were able to express in song their unconscious inner perception of the unseen world.

You desire companionship and like to share vicariously the feelings and experiences of others. However, you should be on your guard against associates who draw from you mentally and physically, causing you to become restless and vacillating in your affairs. When such psychic depletion occurs, you can restore harmony and balance in your life by retiring briefly from contact with people and allowing your mind to seek its own focus, free of the disturbing influences of other people's thoughts.

When Pisces people are subject to prolonged emotional conflicts, they sometimes experience behavioral disorders, such as anxiety reactions, compulsions, sensory disturbances, and phobias. If and when physical symptoms associated with these neuroses manifest themselves, you should try to identify and isolate factors which are known to produce such conditions, and eliminate them. If psychological ill health persists, seek the help of a competent psychiatrist. You respond well to psychoanalysis.

In choosing a vocation which will call forth latent talents, with which you are generously endowed, you should consider those types of employment in which creative imagination, empathy, and diplomacy are required. Depending upon your education and family background, you could fashion a successful career in the theatrical arts; as a novelist, poet, musician; social worker; promoter and publicist; priest; sailor; worker in hospitals, prisons, and religious retreats; and in the medical arts as a pharmacist, therapist, hospital administrator, podiatrist, neurologist, psychiatrist, or nurse.

In love, you are devoted and tender, often assuming a passive role in the relationship, even though you are a man. Owing to the tremendous impact your emotional life has upon your general health, you should be wary of marrying a person whose birth chart maps planetary positions that are inharmonious with yours. As a general rule, among the Sun signs, you will find persons born during the periods corresponding to Cancer, Scorpio, Taurus, and Capricorn the most congenial. The least likely candidates for a successful life union would be Librans, unless individual planetary aspects provide striking evidence to the contrary.

Piscean men and women both possess a strong sex drive, which can sometimes blind them to other important aspects of marriage.

Women of the sign, in particular, when a badly aspected Venus is involved, frequently choose their mates solely on the basis of sexual attraction. In some cases, the native finds an outlet for her excessive libido in mediumship or in religious fervor, which Schrenck-Notzing considers the clinical equivalent of nymphomania.

The Piscean male is also something of a sensualist, who usually seeks sexual adventure with a number of different women. Since they are very magnetic and charming, they do not have to be aggressive to become involved in strange liaisons. Certain women seem to gravitate to them and to get in bed without being invited—at least formally.

The defects of Piscean character almost always stem from weakness and are not traits of an inherently vicious

131

nature. Furthermore, in the proper circumstances and with the right supervision, all can be treated successfully.

To sum up:

Your sign is ruled by Neptune, the mysterious planet of illusion, imagination, idealism, glamour, decay, and extrasensory perception.

You are artistic, passive, self-sacrificing, highly sensitive, and emotional. Jupiter, the co-ruler of Pisces, further emphasizes the expansiveness of your mind and spirit, enabling you to penetrate the barriers of the material universe and to pass beyond into another dimension, or downward into chaos and dissolution.

You possess also to a certain degree the Jupiterian qualities of benevolence, wisdom, spontaneity, and the desire to garner experience.

You have the means at your disposal to forge a great destiny and to influence the future of mankind (as did Piscean Albert Einstein), or to remain wrapped in your dreams. The choice is yours.

PISCEAN DIET AND BIOCHEMISTRY

You require a high-protein diet, which will provide the energy for the proper functioning of cells in your body, without encouraging the Piscean predisposition to retain water in the tissues. Too, protein foods will nourish the skeletal muscles which help give you an erect posture. The moment your daily menu is balanced toward fats and sugars, your posture will begin to suffer. If you go long enough without adequate protein intake, you will note a clearly defined sag in your physique. Your shoulders will begin to go round, and your arches will haven a tendency to flatten out.

You can be reasonably sure that your internal muscular system suffers a similar fate. The abdominal muscles will become flabby, adversely affecting the stomach and bowels, and the other internal organs supported by them. Digestion will be impaired because the intestinal walls do not properly perform their function of passing the food along by means of an undulating motion.

In planning a nutrition program, you can insure an adequate amount of protein if you include in your daily diet such high-protein foods as lean meat, eggs, fish, cheeses, yogurt, and nuts.

Good health depends to a large extent upon having an adequate amount of iron-phosphate—the Pisces cell-salt —in the blood. The body's vitally necessary supply of oxygen is carried by molecules of this salt, which have a chemical affinity for that element.

When there is a deficiency of iron phosphate, you are likely to suffer from anemia, low blood pressure, depression, glandular disorders, dropsy, and dull, throbbing headaches. You may find that you are short of breath following any kind of exertion; or that you tire easily and experience a feeling of general fatigue.

Dr. George Washington Carey, who made extensive studies of biochemistry, including its relation to astrology, wrote that "when these oxygen carriers are deficient, the circulation is increased in order to conduct a sufficient amount of oxygen to the extremities—all parts of the body —with the diminished quantity of iron on hand, exactly as seven men must move faster to do the work of ten."

He notes that this increased motion of the blood causes a rise in body heat, which is identified as inflammation or fever.

Fortunately, iron sulphate is present in a great variety of ordinary foods. However, Ada Muir, an authority on the subject, advises that foods eaten for the purpose of overcoming a deficiency, rather than as maintenance, should not be cooked, since cooking liberates the iron, which is usually thrown away with the water used for cooking.

Iron phosphate foods which can be eaten raw are lettuce, strawberries, radishes, cucumbers, almonds, walnuts, and raisins.

Some cooked foods which are rich in the Piscean cell-salt are spinach, beef liver, lima beans, and lean beef.

Women and children of the sign are more likely to experience iron deficiency than are Piscean men. The reason is that women lose it through menstruation, and children require extra amounts for growth.

In ancient times, Green and Roman physicians tried to remedy iron deficiencies by soaking pieces of that metal in vinegar and giving the resulting infusion to the patient. Such a method of taking iron was ineffective, however, because the element remained in its crude state and did not enter the blood, but was discharged from the body through the bowels.

When taken as a therapeutic supplement in tablet form, phosphate of iron has to be triturated with milk sugar up to the sixth potency before it can be absorbed by the mucous membranes and pass into the blood.

The zodiacal *mineral* of Pisces is organic iodine. Recent studies have shown that a deficiency of this important element is widespread among the country's general population, but among natives of this sign the percentage is higher than average.

A severe lack of iodine causes enlargement of the thyroid glands and an associated condition called myxedema, characterized by extreme dryness of the skin and a disturbance of the body's temperature control system. You may feel cold when other people are warm, for example.

Menopausal women and adolescents are more likely to suffer iodine insufficiency than are male Pisceans.

The best food sources of organic iodine are sea foods and ocean fish. Iodized salt is not a satisfactory source because, to get the amount you need, you would have to ingest large quantities, which would be harmful.

The herbs associated with your sign are Iceland moss, borage, elecampane, and seaweed.

Your homeopathic remedy is *Vertrum.*

YOGA FOR PISCES

Pisces people, more than the natives of almost any other sign (with the possible exception of Cancer), can benefit from the practice of simple yogic breathing. The cosmic energy absorbed by your system by this means will go a long way toward countering the natural passivity and physical weakness indicated in your radical chart.

If you are to derive the maximum good from the exercise, however, you must overcome the thing which makes yoga difficult or unfruitful for most Westerners, namely, impatience. In this age of powerful drugs and instant everything, students expect overnight results from their yogic practice as well.

But the science of health was developed in an Oriental setting, in which the movement of human undertakings, like the stars themselves, was attuned to a great cosmic order, rather than to desires of the individual.

Bear in mind, then, that the following breath-control technique will require time to make its effect known. Perhaps you can take courage from the fact that the Sanskrit name for the exercise is *Vjjayi*, which means the Victorious.

Time: 8 A.M. to 10 A.M.

Place: Well-ventilated room or secluded place outdoors (in the shade).

Duration of practice: Approximately 6 minutes.

Technique: Seated in a comfortable posture, but with the spine straight, close your eyes and calm the mind and senses by trying to feel the deliberate, timeless pulse of creation, vibrating around and through you.

When you are relaxed, inhale deeply a small amount of air (not enough to fill the lungs to capacity), breathing through both nostrils. Hold the breath while you count to five, then close your right nostril, and exhale through

135

the left while counting to ten. Repeat this cycle twelve times during the first few weeks of practice. Later, increase the number of times to twenty.

As you inhale, your breath should produce a sound between nose and throat, like that of air being expelled from a tire that has a small puncture.

Unlike most yogic breathing exercises, this one may be practiced during periods of illness or fatigue.

HOW MEDICAL ASTROLOGY WORKS

THE QUESTION most often posed by scientific opponents of astrology is: What is the material means by which the stars (or energy from the stars) can act upon the human body?

Paracelsus, the great sixteenth-century physician-astrologer, gave the most satisfactory answer to that challenge:

"Man is related to the stars by reason of his sidereal body."

Sidereal, remember, is a synonym for astral, a word which means not only "pertaining to or coming from the stars," but also "designating a kind of supersensible substance alleged to be next above the tangible world in refinement." (Webster's New International Dictionary)

A sidereal (or astral) body, then, is defined as a subtle counterpart of the physical body. It is known to the Hindus as the *linga sharira,* a kind of etheric double which possesses a series of force-centers called *chakras* because they resemble discs or wheels.

According to Eastern teaching, energy received from the cosmos passes from these subtle centers of receptivity into the gross body by means of invisible circuits called *nadis.*

Our hidden centres of celestial force
Open like flowers to a heavenly atmosphere

reads one Hindu text—the *Savitri*.

In the West, particularly in recent times, various writers have identified the *chakras* as the endocrine glands. Such a conclusion is not entirely justified, since the *chakras* are in fact situated in the astral body and are not, strictly speaking, a part of the physical organism.

At the same time, the centers *are* functionally related to the endocrine system, influencing the body by stimulating the ductless glands.

A majority of today's medical astrologers, while ignoring the astral body, recognize the fact that there must be sensitive points in the nervous system through which electromagnetic stellar energy acts upon the body.

One widely accepted theory holds that each endocrine gland, together with its associated nerve plexus, is responsive to the magnetism of a certain planet. For example, the thyroid is believed to be sensitive to the influence of the planet Mercury, the gonads to Uranus, the posterior lobe of the pituitary to Jupiter, and so on.

In keeping with their concept of man as a microcosm ("As above, so below"), esoteric astrologers regard the human structure as an individual solar system. In such a system, the endocrine glands become in miniature the planets for which they have an affinity.

Rodney Collin, the British and disciple of Ouspensky, calls attention to the fact that, in a schematic diagram of the human body, if the heart is taken as the Sun or center of the system, the endocrine glands will lie upon a spiral, just as the solar system appears to be an expanding spiral of planets.

From the heart's Sun-center, the spiral "uncoils through the thymus, the pancreas, the thyroid and parathyroids, the solar plexus, where the adrenals take effect, on to the posterior pituitary and anterior pituitary, and with its final convolution through the sex glands to the pineal body, the ultimate outpost and possibility of the organism."

This view of the human body as a solar system—a microcosm which duplicates or in some way reflects the macrocosm or universe as a whole—was not original with Ouspensky. Readers familiar with the history of philosophy will recognize it as being basically part of the general world view of Aristotle, who received it from his master Plato and from Pythagoras.

The doctrine passed, along with the rest of Aristotelian thought, into the scholastic philosophy of the Middle Ages, where it took root among the alchemists and astrologers, who found in it a rational explanation of natural phenomena.

Later, during the Renaissance, the ill-fated Giordano Bruno (d. 1600), who adopted the Copernican concept of the physical universe, restated the hylozoism of the ancients, declaring that the universe is one organism whose dwelling place is the infinite reaches of space.

The human individual, Bruno said, is a monad which, though existing as a separate, integrating force, becomes conscious of the universe because it has its being in the *Monas monadum*, the world soul which permeates everything.

This notion of the universal individual is again given expression more than half a century after Bruno's death, in the monadology of the German philosopher, Gottfried Wilhelm Leibniz.

In brief, the theory of reality, as formulated by Leibniz, centers on the doctrine of monads, which are indivisible, indestructible units that make up the universe.

But these atomlike beings must not be confused with the dead substance of the materialist. The atomic particles of chemistry and physics are similar, but no two monads are alike. Further, the monad is a center of force, a little universe in itself, reflecting every other monad. It has the inherent power to become conscious as an individual. The human being is such a self-conscious unit.

The extent of consciousness possessed by any individual monad depends upon the degree of clearness with which it reflects or represents all other monads.

In explaining the correspondence of one representation with another, resulting in an over-all harmony of the universal system of monads, Leibniz anticipates Jung's theory of synchronicity by two centuries.

He calls his theory Preestablished Harmony. By this he means that the monads have, from the beginning of time, been endowed with a certain relationship to one another, so that the changes occurring in one monad correspond with preordained changes in every other monad of the system. Monads are like so many individual clocks, accurately preadjusted to keep exactly corresponding time.

It is apparent at once, of course, that Leibniz left little room for free will in his system. However, we will not undertake here a discussion of his principle of conditioned freedom—that is, the self-conscious development of a monad. So far as astrology is concerned, the importance of his thought lies in his characterizing matter as force and individual man as a microcosm.

THOUGHT CELLS AND STELLAR AERIALS

C. C. Zain, who spent many years researching the subject, formulated a theory of stellar anatomy which views the material of the astral body as a *psychoplasm*, composed of thought cells or a totality of previous states of consciousness.

According to Zain, each planet in a birth chart maps an organization of thought cells, which, in effect, becomes a receiving set in the astral body for energy coming from the particular planet so positioned. For example, the location of Mars in the natal chart (by sign and degree) marks a dynamic stellar structure tuned to the astral frequency of the planet Mars. If Mars was in the sign Aries at the time of your birth, the receiving and transmitting center for Martian energy would be situated in the head zone of the astral body.

As a corollary to this postulate, Zain states that each vital thought structure mapped in the birth chart by a planet has a *stellar antenna*. If the planet in question is unaspected, the aerial is analogous to a short loop antenna used in radio or television reception. But when one planet aspects another, the two will be joined by a line extending through the astral body between them. This sidereal line is, so to speak, a permanent built-in antenna, which picks up signals from the planets concerned and transmits them to both terminals. (In the case of a conjunction or parallel, the aerial stretches around the two, rather than between them.)

In addition to the permanent antennas formed by planetary aspects at the time of birth, Zain goes on to assert that temporary aerials are also formed when any planet, by progression, comes within one degree of perfect aspect to another planet in the natal chart.

Another interesting feature of the stellar-antenna theory is the conclusion that any astral energy which has the frequency of a given planet will be picked up by the extra-sensory aerials, whether it emanates from the planet itself, from some object ruled by the planet, or in the form of thought waves from the minds of persons under the same planetary influence.

The question naturally arises: How does planetary energy reaching response-receptors in the astral body affect the physical organism?

The answer lies in the fact that man possesses an electromagnetic body, generated by chemical changes associated with his metabolism. "Astral substance," writes Zain in *Vitality, Health and Disease* (Brotherhood of Light Series No. 106), "including stellar cells, stellar

141

structures and the thoughts which build them, does not communicate its energies directly to physical substance. There is too wide a gulf between the velocities of inner-plane existence and outer-plane existence for these two worlds to affect each other directly. They exchange energies only through that boundary substance which commonly is called electromagnetism."

SCIENCE CONFIRMS BIOMAGNETIC THEORY

Much of Zain's work, based as it is on esoteric principles, lies well beyond the present-day scope of the physical sciences. However, recent laboratory experiments, conducted by a physicist and a surgeon, have demonstrated scientifically the existence of an electromagnetic field encompassing the human body.

The studies were carried out by Dr. Robert O. Becker, previously referred to in the present work, and by his colleague, physicist Charles Bachman.

The two researchers used a hypersensitive electrode device to trace the biomagnetic field surrounding the body. They found that, just as occultists have long maintained, the invisible radiation took roughly an ovoid form, and was somewhat stronger around the brain and spinal cord, diminishing slightly around the lower extremities.

Further, they discovered that the magnetic currents were of both positive and negative polarity. The back of the head and the principal neural plexus along the spine, for example, showed a positive charge, while some other areas, including the forehead, arms, and legs, were negative.

During administration of an ordinary anesthetic, Dr. Becker found that the reading at the forehead gradually shifts from negative to zero (no charge at all).

Becker and Bachman concluded that the magnetic currents detected by their electrodes were connected to the nerve cells and synapses (polarizing "switches") of the cerebro-spinal complex.

Changes in the Earth's magnetic field, caused by interrupting frequencies of the Moon and other planets, affect the central nervous system by altering the body's electromagnetic field.

As reported in an earlier chapter, Dr. Becker has shown that subtle variations in the intensity of our geomagnetic environments are directly correlated with the number of admissions to mental hospitals.

Practitioners of medical astrology know that not only mental illness but all the major ailments of man are influenced by the planetary patterns which produce the ever-shifting magnetic relationship between Earth and the cosmos. They also know that an individual's birth chart will map the time of critical configurations and will designate the part of the body that will be affected.

The work of the two researchers just cited is by no means the only scientific investigation of biomagnetic phenomena to be undertaken in recent times. Similar experiments have been and continue to be carried out in England, western Europe, and in Iron Curtain countries.

It has, in fact, been going on since 1600, when William Gilbert published a book summarizing experiments done up to that time with magnetism, which was considered a universal phenomenon affecting both animate and inanimate life on Earth.

More than a century later, Anton Mesmer, the controversial genius who laid the groundwork for modern psychotherapy, formulated the concept of *animal magnetism*. He defined this force as a subtle magnetic fluid which passes around and through everything.

By fluid, of course, Mesmer did not mean a liquid. His notion of fluid was something consisting of particles which easily flow and change their relative position without separation of the mass itself.

In the thesis which he prepared for his doctorate in

medicine at the University of Vienna, Mesmer advanced the hypothesis that there exists a mutual influence between heavenly bodies, the Earth, and animate bodies, and that it acts through the medium of a "universally distributed and continuous fluid."

He cited the theories of Paracelsus, Newton, and Descartes all reputable thinkers) to support his belief that such a force was physical even though it was invisible. As Newton had said, it was not only the coefficient of gravitation, it also affected the human body by means of vibrations along the filaments of the nerves.

Mesmer's enemies, however, chose to ignore the scientific basis of his work. They concentrated, instead, on the more esoteric aspects of his techniques—the celebrated *baquet*, or huge tub with its protruding iron rods, for patient's to grasp; the long coat of lavender silk which Mesmer wore, and the iron wand he carried; the "mesmeric" passes with the hands to produce a somnambulistic state.

All these things resembled the trappings of quackery and provided the basis for branding him a fraud.

The fact that his melodramatic procedures were highly successful in curing all kinds of illness only made Mesmer the more hated by his less gifted colleagues. He was exposing their avarice and their limitations by treating the poor without fee and by accomplishing remarkable feats in medicine of which they were incapable.

Visual examination of the human field or "aura" was first accomplished by sensitives, who sat in darkened rooms and viewed it with psychic vision.

The best-known researcher in this field was Baron Karl von Reichenbach, a nineteenth-century chemist and metallurgist, who called the emanations from the human body Odyle or odic force.

The first attempt to see the aura with physical sight was made in the early 1920's by Dr. Walter Kilner of St. Thomas Hospital in London. He developed a screen using a rare coal-tar dye called dicyanin, which rendered the body's magnetic radiation visible to ordinary observers.

Dr. Kilner reported that the appearance of the aura changed when a person became ill. He worked out a system of diagnosing disease by observation of these auric variations. For example, the presence of dark spots and certain distortions of the structural pattern indicated nervous disorders. Significantly, the onset of an ailment was presaged by characteristic abnormalities of the aura long before clinical symptoms appeared. Such premonitory signs lend weight to the theory held by many medical astrologers that illness strikes the subtle body first and is then reflected in the physical make-up.

Another curious phenomenon reported in the findings of the London physician was that of strange rays often observed emerging from the body, and shooting off into space. Kilner noted that they always moved in a straight line; and he found that they could be controlled by thought. Later investigators have concluded that these aura-rays are the result of directed consciousness.

The notion of directed consciousness controlling electromagnetic lines of force is important to medical astrology. It provides an explanation of how the individual can modify or alter the train of directions reaching him from planetary sources. It also proves the truth of the axiom that the stars incline, they do not compel.

It is Mercury, the planet of conscious thought and reason, which has the power to change the direction of magnetic currents and to raise or lower their vibratory rate. Acting as a monitor, Mercury thus plays a vital role in the over-all health picture.

Dr. Kilner's work was carried forward by Oscar Bagnall, who developed a new viewing screen using another and much less expensive coal-tar dye known as pinacyanol. (The dye used by Kilner had cost $20 a gram; that of Bagnall, $2.15 a gram.)

In Germany, France, and England, as well as in Soviet

Russia, photoelectric methods of studying the biomagnetic field have been evolved. Generally, their findings confirm the work of Kilner, Bagnall, and others.

GUIDE TO ASTRO-DIAGNOSIS

THE READER who has carefully studied the preceding pages will not need to be reminded that medical astrology is a complex art. Accurate diagnosis of disease by an interpretation of radical and progressed horoscopes requires not only long experience and great skill in astrology but a basic knowledge of medicine as well. Few practicing astrologers today can lay honest claim to such expertise.

The literature, while it provides working guidelines based on traditional sources, is largely of a vintage which predates recent advances in medical science and pharmacology. Too, a great many important texts from the past have been lost or still remain untranslated, locked up in libraries which are not accessible to most students.

It has been only in the last few years that researchers, both in the field of astrology and outside it, have undertaken serious studies which have thrown new light upon man's intimate relation with the cosmos.

As the search for knowledge continues, there is no doubt that many of the long-held aphorisms of *Medicina Astrologica* will be modified or supplanted by new ones. It is very likely, however, that the basic rules of procedure will remain the same, since they provide the necessary framework of reference for any elaboration of the system.

There is general agreement among medical astrologers that the position of and aspects to the Sun, Moon, and ascendant or rising sign constitute the foundation for the

147

delineation of health or for the practice of astro-diagnosis.

In examining the radical chart to determine the native's over-all prospects as regards both vitality and recuperative powers, most experienced astrologers start with the Sun. That is because the Sun's strength at time of birth (by sign and aspect) provides an accurate index to the organic constitution.

It should be borne in mind, however, that vitality and good health do not guarantee longevity. Sometimes a person may enjoy radiant good health all his life, but die at an early age, while another will suffer various illnesses and infirmities and yet live to a ripe old age. The *length* of life is indicated by other factors than those involving solar position. As a general rule, one may reasonably expect a long life if the Sun, Moon, and ascendant are all strong by sign and all (as well as the ascendant's planetary ruler) are free of any affliction.

According to the late Dr. William M. Davidson, the Sun sign and related aspects show the *voltage,* so to speak, of the vital inflowing force, while the Moon and its aspects, together with cross aspects of the malefic planets, determine the amperage or *rate* of flow.

Thus, the Sun's position in the birth chart may give a powerful vitality; but if the electromagnetic solar current flows erratically or irregularly because of the Moon's affliction, the result will be poor health despite the inherent strength of the physical constitution.

Dr. Davidson compared the function of the ascendant or rising sign to that of resistance in an electrical wire. During a series of lectures before a group of professional astrologers in New York, he put it this way:

"In an ordinary electric circuit, you have the flow of current or voltage (Sun); then you have the rate of flow—even or uneven—which is the amperage (Moon); but there is also the resistance of the wire.

"Now the physical body, indicated by the ascending sign, shows the kind of conductivity or resistance offered. It will thus readily be seen why a Capricorn ascendant

(Saturn slowed up) offers more resistance than in the average; hence, these youngsters are rarely robust in infancy, but grow more vigorous as they grow older.

"Gemini, on the other hand, is a ready conductor, and so you find these babies very active, restless and constantly in motion because the conduction, shown by the ascendant, is good.

"Fire signs as ascendants betoken ready conduction. So do air signs, water signs—fair; while earth signs, being more resistant, do not let the vital influx flow so readily.

"Therefore, in judging the general constitution, give attention to the Sun's sign and aspects; planets tenanting the fire signs (affecting the brain and cord); and resistance or conductivity of the ascendant. Then turn to the Moon's sign and aspects, and the sign tenancies and aspects of the malefics to solve the problem of health."

When the radical Sun is well-aspected by Mars, the native will have extraordinary vitality and the inherent power to throw off disease.

If the natal Sun is afflicted by Saturn, on the other hand, or by a square between Sun and Moon, the person will be deficient in constitutional vigor. According to Max Heindel, when such aspects are noted in the birth chart, it is wise during any subsequent illness to closely observe the progressed Moon in aspect to the ill-dignified planets. Transits of the new and full Moons also deserve special attention in such cases.

Most authorities regard the Sun as an especially important index to the general health of males, while the Moon is considered the dominant influence in the nativity of the female.

Diseases caused by afflictions to the Sun are usually of a chronic or serious nature.

INFLUENCE OF THE MOON

Next to the Sun, the Moon is the celestial body which

149

exerts the most direct and powerful influence on the human organism.

The female menstrual cycle coincides with the duration of a lunar month; and the normal period from conception to delivery of the human young corresponds to nine lunar months.

As previously noted in connection with the experiments of Dr. Robert O. Archer and others, the different phases of the Moon mark the onset and crises of various illnesses —especially mental disorders.

Qualitatively, the Moon is feminine, negative, magnetic, cold, moist, fruitful, lymphatic, and inconstant.

She is the collector of solar energy, reflecting the heat and light of the Sun and, by her swift course through the twelve zodiacal signs each month, is a distributor of that luminary's forces as well as those of other planets she transits and aspects.

We have noted that, in the human body, she controls the rate of flow (comparable to amperage) of electrical solar energy. When weak by sign, house position, and aspects, the flow will be uneven and, in consequence, the native will be predisposed to functional illnesses, even though he may have a strong Sun.

Traditional astrologers say that the Moon is weak if above the horizon in a day nativity or below the horizon in the geniture of a person born at night.

Cancer is the home of the Moon and the only sign in the zodiac ruled by her. She has her exaltation in Taurus, her detriment in Capricorn, and her fall in Scorpio. She is harmonious with the watery signs Cancer and Pisces; and with Gemini, Libra, and Aquarius.

It was long thought that the Moon rules the first seven years of a child's life; but some modern writers have challenged that belief. Be that as it may, there is statistical evidence to support the theory that lunar afflictions are more serious in childhood than in later life.

The Moon is said to afflict by her square or opposition aspects, especially to the malefics. In the natal horoscope, her influence is considered to be benefic when she is waxing and, *per contra*, somewhat adverse (although weaker) in her action when she is waning.

Dr. Howard Cornell states, without citing his authority, that a child born at the instant of a full Moon—especially if it is female—usually dies at the next full moon.

DISEASES INDICATED BY LUNAR AFFLICTIONS

In considering the over-all rulership of the Moon and, consequently, of the parts of the body likely to be affected when that planet is badly aspected, attention centers on the fluidic and lymphatic system, the stomach and alimentary tract, thymus gland, left eye in the male and right eye in the female, ovaries and uterus, medulla oblongata, and the dissolving processes of the body.

The Moon engenders and rules all acute or acquired diseases and those which come and go periodically.

Disease tendencies most frequently involving evil aspects to the Moon in the various zodiacal signs are given below. These are general guidelines for delineation. For more specific indications, see the diagnostic configurations for common disorders listed alphabetically in the last chapter of this book.

Moon in Aries: Defects of vision, migraine headache, insomnia, improper functioning of the posterior pituitary, brain fever, mental strain, and baldness.

Moon in Taurus: Quinsy, aphthous ulcers, septic sore throat, pains in the legs and feet, eye disorders (if in Taurus 29° and afflicted by one of the malefics or higher-octave planets), and (by reflex action into Scorpio) menstrual troubles.

Moon in Gemini: Edema of the lungs, rheumatism in arms and shoulders, bronchitis, asthma, pneumonia, and aneurisms.

Moon in Cancer: Stomach troubles, dropsy, digestive

151

disorders, obesity, hysteria, and (when severely afflicted) carcinoma.

Moon in Leo: Backaches, convulsions, circulatory disorders, heart trouble, and (when in the manger of the Ascelli—6° 7' Leo) impairment of sight, especially in the left eye.

Moon in Virgo: Abdominal tumors, disorders of the bowels, dysentery, and (if in 22° Virgo) appendicitis.

Moon in Libra: Abscesses, kidney troubles, pleurisy, uremia, tendency to Bright's disease, goiter, homosexuality (when afflicted by Uranus), and headaches (by reflex action into Aries).

Moon in Scorpio: Danger of poison, irregular menstruation, diseases of the generative organs, bladder complaints, hernial aneurism, hydrocele and (by reflex) throat troubles.

Moon in Sagittarius: Gout, hip injuries and diseases, sciatica, paralysis, and (by reflex) asthma.

Moon in Capricorn: Rheumatism, deficiency of synovial fluid, psoriasis, digestive disorders, and skin eruptions.

Moon in Aquarius: Disturbed circulation (especially in the lower limbs), delirium tremens (from alcoholism), varicose veins, syncope, and dropsy.

Moon in Pisces: Pains and cramps in the feet, tendency to the drug habit, poor circulation in the extremities, dropsy, psychosomatic ailments.

THE ASCENDANT OR RISING SIGN

In determining an individual's general health and the diseases to which he will be susceptible at one time or another during his lifetime, it is essential to know his ascendant or rising sign.

The ascendant is the sign rising on the eastern horizon at the moment of birth (owing to the rotation of Earth on its axis), and as seen from the birthplace. The term is also used to designate not just the exact degree of the ecliptic which is rising, but the entire zodiacal sign to which the rising degree belongs.

Earth is in continuous motion, of course, with the result that a different degree of the ecliptic appears over the horizon every four minutes. Thus, if twins were born more than four minutes apart (as they often are), they would have different rising degrees. If the first infant's ascendant were 30° Taurus, his twin would have a different *sign* of the zodiac as an ascendant, namely, Gemini.

Hence the importance of accurately establishing the ascendant in an individual's horoscope. In the case of medical astrology, with which we are presently concerned, exact determination of the rising sign is especially serious because it is used to mark the cusp of the First House, which is concerned with the physical body.

C. C. Zain, whose theory of stellar antennas we have already discussed, asserted that the degree on the ascendant maps a heavy line of electromagnetic energy running the astral body, clearly visible to persons who have clairvoyant vision. Aspects of this "ground wire" are almost as important, where health matters are concerned, as aspects to the Sun and Moon.

Establishing the ascendant for children born in the United States today is a fairly simple matter because the birth usually takes place in a maternity hospital where the exact time of the event is recorded.

However, the great majority of people do not know the precise hour (to say nothing of the minute) of their birth. Even parents, when still living, are surprisingly vague when asked to recall the exact time their offspring first saw the light.

Practicing astrologers use several methods to solve this problem. One is known as rectification. This is done by calculations based on directions timed to important events in the native's life, such as first serious illness, accidents, death of a parent or sibling, marriage, birth of a child, and so on.

Another involves comparing the house positions and

153

aspects in the individual's horoscope with his social standing, traits of character, kind of job or profession, and financial status.

A third procedure is one known as the Prenatal Epoch, developed from an ancient Hermetic theorem. Hermes notes that a certain necessary relationship exists between the place of the moon at birth and the ascendant at the time of conception, or vice versa. Sepharial in 1898 worked out an astronomical formula based on this general idea and published it under the title, *The Prenatal Epoch and the Law of Sex.*

Experienced astrologers also become very adept at identifying a person's ascendant by his physical appearance, mannerisms, and voice.

An instance of the kind not long ago involved the writer. During an interview with the editor of the *Rosicrucian Magazine,* published by the Rosicrucian Fellowship of Oceanside, California, I chanced to mention that my rising sign was Virgo. The editor—a lady of considerable expertise in things astrological—said quietly but firmly that my ascendant was not Virgo, but Leo. Later, when I learned the exact time of my birth, it turned out that she was right. I had previously been misinformed about the natal hour.

The late Dr. W. M. Davidson, who, as a doctor of medicine, used astrology in his practice, over the years compiled a list of salient features by which he claimed to be able unerringly to identify anyone's ascendant. His references points follow:

Aries Rising: The hairline comes down on the forehead in a kind of widow's peak. The eyebrows usually meet. The Adam's apple goes up and down when the person talks.

Taurus Rising: The most characteristic feature is a kind of pop-eyeness and a roundness of forehead. Dr. Davidson cites President Eisenhower as typical. The president's mother, who consulted Dr. Davidson on the matter, could

154

not recall the hour of birth, but the physician assured her that Ike had a Taurean-ascendant.

Gemini Rising: There is usually a tendency toward a slightly aquiline nose, sometimes even suggestive of a bird beak. Another typical feature is a mobile lip. The over-all impression of the facial expression is what might be called a cat-swallowed-the-canary look.

Cancer Rising: Gives a compressed mouth, like a slit. Viewing the face from the side, it appears somewhat flat and round, like a full moon.

Leo Rising: Look for a broadness of shoulders and certain cock of the head. The native projects a feeling of vitality and lively spirit.

Virgo Rising: The most striking evidence of a Virgo ascendant is the high, domed head, which is not very broad. Sometimes the face is triangular; and often the native will have a pointed, forward chin.

Libra Rising: Venus, the planetary ruler of Libra, usually gives a clear skin. The eyes seem to look into distance, and there is an other-worldly or somewhat bemused air about the person who has a Libra ascendant.

Scorpio Rising: As a rule, a Scorpio ascendant is indicated by a very heavy eyebrow, a strong voice, and a penetrating eye. The upper lip frequently tends to fold. The nose is rarely straight; it may be either Roman or retroussé. Open pores on the back of the hand are another distinguishing feature.

Sagittarius Rising: When this arc of the zodiac is ascending at birth, according to Dr. Davidson, it will result in a person's having a straight nose, with the distance between root and tip somewhat longer than average, and a slight fullness of the eye—not as prominent as that of the Taurus ascendant, which bulges somewhat. The legs are rather long in proportion to the torso.

Capricorn Rising: One of the most common telltale signs of a Capricorn ascendant are ears that grow directly into the cheek bones without forming lobes. Women born at this time usually have prominent veins on the backs of

155

their hands, even in early life. Natives of both sexes are likely to have scanty hair.

Aquarius Rising: Wavy hair and a straight eye angle are the principal clues to a person having Aquarius on the ascendant at birth. To these two characteristics, Dr. Davidson adds a third—"a friendly eye."

Pisces Rising: Those born when Pisces was rising can be recognized by their flat-footed walk and by the fact that generally the white of the eye shows between the iris and the lower lid. Being under the influence of the mysterious planet Neptune, their manner often suggests a preoccupation with secret thoughts.

CALCULATING LOCAL SIDEREAL TIME

Even when the exact time of birth is known in terms of local time, further calculations are necessary to determine the rising sign. These computations are fairly complex, involving several steps—determination of true local time of birth, conversion of local time to Greenwich Sidereal Time, and adjustment to local sidereal time because of difference in longitude between Greenwich and the birthplace.

If you are a beginner in astrology and attempt this task yourself, you should check your findings with an experienced astrologer.

For readers unfamiliar with the procedure involved in casting a horoscope, the best course to follow is to have your natal chart set up by a competent professional. Among the vital data given on such a birth map will be the ascendant, including the degree of the rising sign.

For quick reference, an easy-to-use *Zodiacal Indicator* in the form of a movable dial mounted on a reference disk was developed by an organization called Esoteric Fraternity in Applegate, California 95703. (I paid $2 for one which I purchased in a bookstore. I do not know whether the price is the same when the device is ordered by mail from the Fraternity.)

Another way in which you can quickly ascertain your rising sign is to consult the Table of Ascendants, included in this book as Appendix V. The table is not intended for determining the exact *degree* of the rising sign, but only your ascendant.

Unless the ascendant is known, it is impossible to erect an accurate birth chart. The reason is that, as previously stated, the rising degree is the fixed point on the horoscope

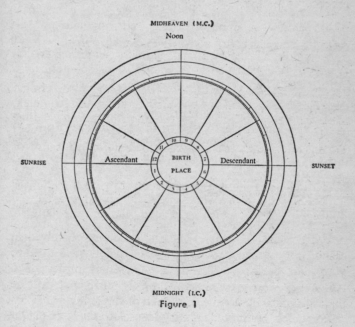

MIDHEAVEN (M.C.)
Noon

SUNRISE

Ascendant

BIRTH
PLACE

Descendant

SUNSET

MIDNIGHT (I.C.)
Figure 1

wheel which marks the beginning of the twelve divisions of the figure, known as *Houses*. (See Figure 1.) Thus, if the zodiacal sign appearing on the eastern horizon when you were born happened to be Leo, the things signified by the First House will be stamped with the character of that sign.

With Leo thus on the cusp of the First House, the succeeding houses will follow in the regular order of the zodiac—Virgo on the Second, Libra on the Third, and so on.

The opposite sign on the East-West axis of the horoscope, which is falling below the western horizon at the same time the ascendant is rising in the East, is called the *descendant*. (In the case of a Leo ascendant, it would be Aquarius.)

The horoscope figure is also bisected along a North-South axis. The upper meridian, corresponding to the North, is designated the *Medium Coeli,* which is Latin for "middle of the heavens," usually indicated by the abbreviation M.C. The lower meridian or southern point of the axis at the bottom of the wheel is called the *Imum Coeli*—I.C.—or "lowest part of the heavens."

The four points—ascendant, descendant, M.C. and I.C. —are the four angles of the birth chart. They are dominant factors in the delineation of any horoscope because a planet posited on an angle has more power than in any other place.

During one's lifetime, when a planet passes over these points of acute receptivity, one is stimulated according to the nature of the transiting planet's influence. Charles E. Carter, an authority on the subject, writes: "The arrival of any malefic on an angle is a critical period, according to the general tenor of the map."

Planets in angular houses—1, 4, 7, 10—are referred to as being *prominent* in the horoscope, and when they are ill-aspected by one of the malefics (Saturn, Mars, Uranus, Neptune, and Pluto) they are said to be "afflicted." The aspects that afflict are the square, opposition, parallel, and in many instances, the conjunction.

All traditional texts state that the two houses most closely related to matters of health and disease are the

158

First and Sixth. This is especially true when they are tenanted—that is, when one or more planets are positioned in the house. When there is no planet in these houses, some astrologers base their diagnosis on the planet ruling the sign on the house's cusp. However, this is not a very satisfactory or accurate method.

A nineteenth-century English authority even questioned the validity of judging health on the basis of Sixth House configurations. James Wilson, in his *Complete Dictionary of Astrology,* wrote: "The cause why the ascendant operates upon the human constitution is unknown, but experience proves it has some effect. It does not so clearly appear that the west angle has any such influence, and still less that the sixth house can be the place from whence we can judge of disease."

Wilson's opinion notwithstanding, the collective experience of most practitioners indicates that the Sixth House provides a guide to the delineation of disease. As a matter of routine procedure, the astro-diagnostician checks the nativity chart to see what planets, if any, are posited in the Sixth House: and whether such planets afflict the luminaries, the ascendant or planets in the First House.

He also ascertains the planetary ruler of the sign on the Sixth-House cusp, takes note of what sign and house it occupies in the horoscope, and then determines which diseases that sign represents and the parts of the body related to it.

His next step is to learn what planets are aspecting the ruler of the Sixth House, as well as the kind of aspect— whether conjunction, parallel, square, sextile, trine, etc.

These data provide a preliminary foundation for a general delineation of potential illnesses.

INFLUENCE OF THE FIRST HOUSE

The First House also holds considerable interest for the medical astrologer because it is dominated by the rising sign, which defines vitality and the inherent strength or weakness of the physical constitution. The ascendant also provides a key to the native's will and personality—his adjustment to his environment.

By a careful analysis of the First House, the experienced astrologer is able to judge the basic emotional pattern, personal habits, thrust of the individual's desires and their gratification, and his ability to discipline himself.

All these factors have a direct bearing on health because behavioral tendencies—whether positive or negative, constructive or destructive—can and do cause illness.

Moreover, if sufficient self-mastery and moral strength are discernible in the natal First House, there is a good chance that the person can modify or overcome pathological tendencies indicated in the Sixth House. For example, unresolved inner conflicts that cause nervous or organic disease may be eliminated by a conscious effort on the part of the individual who has the will to change the character defects which caused them. Wrong diet can be corrected. Inharmonious personal relationships can be changed. Discordant conditions of employment, place of residence, and so on, can be remedied.

The Third and Ninth houses are closely related to mental disorders and, consequently, deserve special scrutiny by the astro-diagnostician on the principle that many diseases are of psychogenic origin.

THE ROLE OF HEREDITY

The question of heredity is also important in the consideration of innate physical weaknesses and predisposition toward certain ailments. This fact may come as a surprise to the critics of the art, who have long maintained that judgment of a person's physical make-up and weaknesses on the basis of a horoscope is nonsense, because these things are largely predetermined by the genetic factor.

As a matter of fact, recent statistical studies, undertaken by scientific nonbelievers in astrology, have shown that heredity itself appears to correspond to stellar patterns.

One such study was made by Michel Gauquelin, a French researcher at the Sorbonne, who set out to disprove astrology and ended up trying to capture it for "real science." He discovered that there is a marked tendency for children to be born in certain cosmic conditions similar to those which prevailed at the birth of their parents.

In other words, the planetary positions and aspects, especially as regards the ascendant, are favorable to the hereditary predisposition to be expected of children born to those particular parents.

Gauquelin based his findings on a statistical evaluation of 30,000 birth charts. Still, he was reluctant to accept the evidence of his studies because of what he termed their "pseudo-astrological flavor." Blind disbeliever to the last, he called the results "inexplicable."

Sepharial's *New Dictionary of Astrology* notes that the theory of planetary heredity is easy to prove by erecting a composite horoscope of every family member, so that planets posited in the same signs will be brought together.

"It is then seen that there is a dominant group influence exerted from one sign more than the others, and to this sign the typal form of the family belongs."

The composite nativity should include the ascendant in the respective horoscopes as though it were a planet rising in the same degree.

For the medical astrologer, interest centers especially upon the prenatal epoch; the position of and aspects to the Sun in the natal map; and the Fourth and Tenth Houses.

If the Sun at birth is in the Earth or water signs (Taurus, Virgo, Capricorn; Cancer, Scorpio, Pisces), or if there is a planetary emphasis of these signs, heredity factors are usually strongest from the mother's side.

When the natal Sun is in the air or fire signs (Gemini,

161

Libra, Aquarius; Aries, Leo, Sagittarius), or these are prominent because of planetary tenancy, inherited traits and tendencies are predominantly from the father's side.

When both Sun and Moon are posited in the same element at birth, the planetary rulers of signs on the cusps of the Fourth and Tenth Houses represent father and mother, respectively.

According to some writers, a predisposition toward inherited disease is indicated by the presence of Scorpio on the cusp of the Fourth House at birth. However, hereditary weaknesses are sometimes involved in afflictions to planets in the fixed signs.

A well-aspected Jupiter in one of the earthly signs at birth, on the other hand, is believed to signify a well-descended body, free of hereditary taint. The same is true when the lord of the geniture is positioned in his own triplicity and not afflicted.

In its deeper implications, planetary heredity involves the controversial question of reincarnation, a subject most modern astrologers like to give a wide berth.

Early writers, and those who are of the esoteric school, however, insist that astrology and the doctrine of rebirth are interrelated. Dr. H. L. Cornell explains it this way:

"Nature and the higher powers so rule, arrange and manage the incarnation of an individual and by the law of attraction and similars, lead an incoming Ego to parents, ancestors and a line of descent which are more or less bound up with the native from out of the past."

These lords of destiny, said Dr. Cornell, cause the birth to occur at a time and place which give a star map of birth in harmony with such familial relationships.

"The parents give to the maturing embryo and child a body much like their own as a rule, or similar to some relative or ancestor in the line; but occult masters and initiates teach that the mind and character of the child are not directly transmitted from the parents."

Instead, the incoming Ego or spirit brings its own individual character with it.

162

"It is said that the star map of birth shows the character and attainments which the native had at his death in the physical body in his material incarnation previous to this one. In the present life, he is forming and building the map which will be . . . a prototype for his next incarnation."

PROGRESSIONS, TRANSITS, AND LUNATIONS

To predict the time that a disease indicated in the natal chart may strike, it is necessary for the astrologer to calculate exactly when transiting planets will stimulate the birth sensitivity related to it. Lunations (the period between one new moon and the next) and eclipses are likewise taken into account.

Using an ephemeris for any given year, the astrologer notes the days when the Sun will pass over conjunctions and oppositions of the natal planets.

According to an ancient aphorism in astrodiagnosis, an individual usually falls ill when either of the two Lights (Sun or Moon) is in the place or in square or opposition to the place occupied by Saturn or Mars at the time of one's birth.

A corollary states that the same is true when either Saturn or Mars is in the place or is in square or opposition to the place, occupied by Sun, Moon, or ascendant at the moment of birth.

During such transits of Mars, the native is in danger of accidents and injuries, especially during travel.

GOOD AND BAD TIMES FOR MEDICATION

In ancient times, when all physicians were also astrologers, medicines were administered to patients according to guidelines indicating times when planetary aspects favored the therapeutic action of the remedies.

As a general rule, a period when the Moon is in the sign of Cancer or Pisces (or the hours of the day governed by their planetary rulers) was considered the best time to take any medicine. Other favorable times are when Jupiter or Venus is rising; or during the hours ruled by Venus or Mercury.

According to the classical tradition, medicine taken during the dominant influence of Saturn would harm rather than help the patient.

Medication was strictly proscribed also when the Moon was passing through one of the ruminant signs (Aries, Taurus, and Capricorn).

Before giving any drug which might disturb the heart function, the physician trained in medical astrology studies the radical chart to determine whether any inherent weakness in that organ would make such a treatment dangerous. A similar analysis is made to assess possible damage to other vital organs on the same basis. Such a procedure is in striking contrast to the methods of orthodox medicine today. As previously noted in this book, hundreds of thousands are made sick each year (and some are killed outright) by the carelessness or ignorance of doctors in prescribing powerful drugs.

Persons in whose natus Neptune is prominent or is afflicted in the Sixth House, should always exercise great caution in taking any kind of medicine, as that configuration predisposes them to illness from drugs. The same is true when Neptune is in square or opposition to Saturn.

Astrologically oriented physicians often check the sign on the cusp of the Fifth House, as well as the sign's planetary ruler, to determine whether a proposed remedy is the proper one.

It is said that, when the planetary ruler of the sign on the eighth cusp is posited in the Sixth House, there is danger that the physician will inadvertently give the patient the wrong medicine.

Early writers on astrology taught that each disease that afflicts mankind had its time and place of birth just as

164

living creatures do. In the area of the Earth where it had its origin, there is also an antidote or remedy for that particular malady. According to the theory, these local specifics are very effective in treating the disease. The remedy may be in the form of an herb, natural foods, or a mineral produced in the region native to the ailment.

Modern practitioners are inclined to use astrology as a valuable aid in diagnosis, but to prescribe drugs made available to us by the recent advances in pharmacology. For long-term therapy and for deficiency diseases, however, dietary supplements, vitamins, and minerals are still the treatment of choice.

Again, it is necessary to remind the reader that, in making any important judgment regarding health or disease, one must consider the *Signature rerum* or stellar pattern as a totality.

This is a complex undertaking, which requires years of experience. It cannot safely be left in the hands of a novice, or entrusted to the limited expertise of a professional who is untrained in medical astrology.

THE END OF LIFE

Astrologers of the past had one striking characteristic in common—the cocksure way they predicted the exact time of such vital events as fatal accidents and death.

Either they were in possession of data not available to us today or they based their prognoses upon some form of extrasensory perception. In either case, there is no evidence to show that their record of accuracy was something to be envied.

Today, no ethical astrologer will undertake to tell a client the precise date of his or of anyone else's demise. For one thing, such a prediction would be a legal offense, punishable by fine and possible imprisonment. For another, any experienced astrologer knows that there is no planetary configuration which presages certain death on a certain day.

There are, of course, indications, both in the radix and in the progressed chart which, to an expert, clearly forewarn that at a given period in the native's life the Significator and vital points of his horoscope will be afflicted by a train of evil directions which *could* cause death. But these alone are not sufficient to make a firm and reliable judgment. As Evangeline Adams once pointed out, according to theories of the ancients, it is a very good year when an individual might not die at least three times.

She added wryly, "There is certainly never any difficulty in discovering why he did die after he is comfortably buried."

Replying to the question of a reader, editors of *The Rosicrucian Fellowship Magazine* recently wrote: "The time of dying is *not* given in the horoscope. This is a common delusion. The horoscope merely indicates the periods during which a person will be under heavy physical or nervous strain, but it positively does not indicate whether or not he will succumb to it. There are numberless incidents in which the horoscope showed what appeared to be almost overwhelming influences brought to bear at a certain time apparently indicating death and through which the person lived quite comfortably. There are numberless other instances in which people died at periods where the horoscope, according to the ordinary rules, showed comparatively little strain."

All this is not to say that there is not a foreordained time in the earthly life of every person when he must make the transition from one kind of existence to another. There are persuasive arguments that the author of *Ecclesiastes* was correct when he asserted that there is a time to every purpose under heaven, "a time to be born and a time to die."

However, the horoscope is not the place to look for the latter of these two vital statistics.

What *can* be ascertained, by a certain amount of skill

and patience, is the probable cause or causes of death; the *threat* of serious or fatal accidents; the circumstances of the final years of life; and disposition of the physical remains, including the location of the grave.

Grisly enough? Then let us not press for the ultimate answer, the exact and fated moment that it will happen. As the late T. S. Eliot noted in one of his poems:

"To apprehend / The point of intersection of the timeless / With time is an occupation for the saint."

PLANETARY PATHOLOGY

DIAGNOSING ILLNESS from a horoscope involves a deductive method of delineation, proceeding from the general to the particular.

As we have seen in the preceding pages, this means that after taking note of the native's general category—the Sun sign—the medical astrologer turns his attention to the Sun, Moon, ascendant, and the four angles of the natal figure. From this examination, he learns at the outset the degree of inherited constitutional vigor, flow of vital force, and mentality of the individual. He learns where the general emphasis on health lies, and how long the person may be expected to live.

Next, he scrutinizes those houses traditionally associated with health and disease, observing where they are tenanted and if so, by which planets; by what aspects these planets are linked to others in the horoscope; the sign on the cusp of the house in question, and the location of the planet.

After making these determinations, he looks to the place, by sign, of every planet in the figure. When these bodies are afflicted by adverse aspects to other planets, especially the malefics, certain ailments or infirmities may be expected. These will correspond to the sign position of the planet.

It must be borne in mind that such horoscopical factors are of a preliminary and general nature. They help pinpoint innate tendencies and offer clues which may serve to disclose the origin of otherwise baffling symptoms.

No final judgment regarding a particular malady should be made, without reference to a diagnostic pattern for that specific syndrome or disease entity, as listed alphabetically in the next chapter of this book.

THE DISEASES OF MERCURY

The influence of Mercury on health is of prime importance in any chart. Whereas the Moon regulates the flow of vital energy in the body, Mercury can change the direction of the electromagnetic currents (hence, their polarity), as well as raise or lower their vibratory rate. This modification is accomplished by a process of conscious thought. When Mercury is afflicted, and negative or discordant thought patterns are established, ailments manifest themselves in those parts of the body indicated by Mercury's position by sign and degree.

Mercury in Aries: Vertigo, neuralgia, nervous breakdown, brain fever, astigmatism, front pituitary, and (by reflex action into Libra) functional disorders of the kidneys.

Mercury in Taurus: Speech impediments, hoarseness, deafness, parathyroid imbalance, and (by reflex action into Scorpio) nervous disturbances of the genitourinary function.

Mercury in Gemini: Gouty pains in the arms, hands, and shoulders; bilious flatulence, bronchitis, asthma, pleurisy, intercostal neuralgia, and (by reflex action into Sagittarius) hip pains.

Mercury in Cancer: Stomach cramps, nervous indigestion, flatulence, alcoholism, and tendency toward catching colds.

Mercury in Leo: Heart palpitation, low back pain, convulsions, fainting spells.

Mercury in Virgo: Diarrhea, colic, nervous debility, asthma (especially in 4° Virgo), shortness of breath.

Mercury in Libra: Renal paroxysms, suppression of the urine, lumbago, nervous headache.

Mercury in Scorpio: Neuralgic pain in the bladder and genitals, menstrual troubles, stuttering, neuritis in the arms and hands.

Mercury in Sagittarius: Sciatic neuritis; chronic coughs; pains in hips, thighs, and knee joints; nervous disorders.

Mercury in Capricorn: Rheumatism, pruritis, back pains, acne, melancholia, anxiety neurosis, and (by reflex action into Cancer) nervous indigestion.

Mercury in Aquarius: Circulatory troubles, varicose veins, shooting pains in various parts of the body, allergies, acidosis, diseases involving the nerve fluids.

Mercury in Pisces: Phthisis, chilblains, temporary amnesia, lassitude, and (by reflex action into Leo) cardiac arrythmia.

THE DISEASES OF VENUS

Venus, being the planet which holds dominion over social affairs, art, romance, and entertainment, is responsible (when badly afflicted) for maladies proceeding from or related to those activities. Consequently, we have ailments caused by dietary indiscretions, sexual promiscuity, irregular habits, and lack of physical exercise.

Pathogenic effects of an afflicted Venus in each of the twelve zodiacal signs are:

Venus in Aries: Rhinitis, head colds, eczema affecting

170

the face, headaches caused by toxemia; and (by reflex action into Libra) kidney complaints.

Venus in Taurus: Swellings of the neck glands, exophthalmic goiter, tonsilitis, mumps, bronchocele; and (by reflex into the opposite sign of Scorpio) venereal diseases or other affections involving the genitals.

Venus in Gemini: Pulmonary inefficiency, dropsy, papilloma, whitlows, elevated lipid level in the blood (which is not in itself a disease, but is believed to be implicated in atherosclerosis).

Venus in Cancer: Irritation of the stomach walls, gastric tumor, attacks of nausea, dyspepsia, cysts, obesity.

Venus in Leo: Spinal ailments, diseases of the aorta, enlarged heart, maladies affecting the middle dorsal nerves.

Venus in Virgo: Peritonitis, diarrhea, tumors, intestinal worms in children, peristaltic debility.

Venus in Libra: Bilious flatulence, uremia, Fallopian pregnancies, renal spasms, anuria.

Venus in Scorpio: Prolapsed uterus, bladder weakness, syphilis, varicocele, uterine tumor, inguinal hernia, and (by reflex action into Taurus) chronic sore throat.

Venus in Sagittarius: Serum hepatitis, enlargement of the liver, tumors in the hip, leg cramps, and (by reflex action into Gemini) respiratory ailments.

Venus in Capricorn: Gouty pains in the knees, skin eruptions, bursitis, herpes zoster (shingles), loss of teeth.

Venus in Aquarius: Glandular dysfunction, varicose veins, leg spasms and swollen ankles, psychosomatic illnesses stemming from an inharmonious marital relationship.

Venus in Pisces: Diseases which attack the feet, abdominal tumors (by reflex action into Virgo), obsession, endocrine imbalance, gonorrhea, fungus growths.

THE DISEASES OF MARS

Mars is traditionally classified as a malefic—that is, a planet which exerts a harmful influence wherever he is found in a nativity, but more particularly when he is placed in discordant aspect to another planet.

While it is true that the powerful action of Mars often provides the energy which triggers many human ills, he can also exert a constructive influence. It is he, along with the Sun, that gives heat and vitality to the body. "In the maintenance of life," wrote Max Heindel, "Mars ever aims to cleanse the body of filth and waste accumulation so that the fires of life may burn brightly. Hence, when the gourmandizing habits of Jupiter and Venus have clogged the system, or the obstructive tendencies of Saturn have poisoned the body by stoppage of elimination, Mars lights the fire of fever and inflammation to burn out the refuse and give the system a new lease on life and energy."

The pathogenic action of Mars predisposes to sudden, inflammatory, acute diseases, in contrast to Saturn, which tends to slow, cold, chronic maladies. Of these two chief afflictors, Saturn is the more insidious.

Some writers say that the Red Planet's influence is more dangerous during the so-called Mars period of life—that is, from the 42nd to the 56th year.

The diseases of Mars, when he afflicts in the twelve signs, are:

Mars in Aries: Cerebral hemorrhage, delirium, facial neuralgia, smallpox, sunstroke, shooting pains in the head, wounds to the head and face, ringworm, insomnia, brain fever, renal hemorrhage (by reflex action into Libra).

Mars in Taurus: Diphtheria, tonsilitis, adenoids, mumps, laryngitis, epithelioma, acne rosacea, polypus, epistaxis (nosebleed); by reflex action into Scorpio: prostrate troubles, venereal ulcers, excessive menstruation, muscular rheumatism in the neck, pharyngitis.

Mars in Gemini: Pneumonia; skin disorders; blows; cuts and wounds to arms, shoulders, and hands; bilious diarrhea; neuritis; inflammation of the lungs; bronchitis; hemoptysis. By reflex action into Sagittarius: sciatica.

Mars in Cancer: Stomach ulcers, dyspepsia, schirrus of the breasts, sexual excesses or perversions, dry cough, gastritis, tumors.

Mars in Leo: Angina pectoris, enlarged heart, palpitation, pericarditis, muscular rheumatism in the back, herpes zoster, aneurism.

Mars in Virgo: Dysentery, gastroenteritis, typhoid, ventral hernia, cholera, appendicitis, pinworms, inflammation of the bowels.

Mars in Libra: Kidney stones, anuria, nephritis, typhus, pyelitis.

Mars in Scorpio: Scarlatina, menorrhagia, vaginitis, uretritis, hypertrophy of the prostrate, ulceration of the ovaries and uterus, varicocele, hemorrhoids, scrotal hernia, scalding urine. By reflex action into Taurus: laryngitis.

Mars in Sagittarius: Sciatica, enteric fever, hip fractures, ulcers, of the thigh. By reflex action into Gemini: pneumonia.

Mars in Capricorn: Rheumatic fever, carbuncles, urticaria, anthrax, pruritis, erysipelas, smallpox, psoriasis, measles, scabies, contusions. By reflex action into Cancer: stomach ulcers.

Mars in Aquarius: Blood poisoning, fractures of the lower leg. By reflex action into Leo: syncope and coronary thrombosis.

Mars in Pisces: Accidents involving the feet; bunions, corns, bromidrosis, foot deformities. By reflex action into Virgo: inflammation of the bowels.

THE DISEASES OF JUPITER

Jupiter, the largest planet in the solar system, with a mass 318 times that of Earth, is known to classical astrology as the Greater Benefic because the nature of his influence (when strong and dignified) is benevolent.

However, as Dr. W. J. Tucker has observed, sometimes the benefics (Jupiter and Venus) are stealthy killers, being implicated in the development of coronary thrombosis and degenerative diseases when configurated with malefics.

The focal point of Jupiter's activity in the body is the liver. There sugar in the form of a substance called glycogen is stored until it is needed as fuel for muscular activity. The liver also acts to remove poisons and foreign substances from the blood. The functions of this vital organ are so important to health that, when it is not working properly, serious illnesses can result.

Astrologically, Jupiter is represented in the diagnostic pattern of diseases arising from congestion or obstructions in the arterial system, disorders involving fats and glycogen, and pathology concerned with the production and secretion of insulin by the pancreas.

The diseases of Jupiter, when badly aspected in the various zodiacal signs, are:

Jupiter in Aries: Vertigo, thromboses, ulcers on the upper gums, fainting, cerebral congestion. By reflex action into Libra: diabetes.

Jupiter in Taurus: Ailments proceeding from gourmandizing, apoplexy, coryza, carbuncles.

Jupiter in Gemini: Pleurisy, lung ailments, fatty degeneration of the liver, pulmonary embolism, and by reflex action into Sagittarius, rheumatism in the hips and thighs.

Jupiter in Cancer: Torpid liver, dyspepsia, stomach dilation from overindulgence, jaundice, blood impurities, dropsy, disturbances of the milk glands. By reflex action into Capricorn, skin eruptions.

Jupiter in Leo: Fatty degeneration of the heart, circulatory disorders, palpitation, cerebral hemorrhage.

Jupiter in Virgo: Abscess of the liver, intestinal disorders, jaundice, fatty degeneration of the liver, lung affections.

Jupiter in Libra: Skin problems, kidney complaints, poor veinous circulation, adrenal insufficiency, renal abscess, morbid changes in the blood, tumors.

Jupiter in Scorpio: Piles, disorders of the genitourinary tract, uterine tumors, hydremia, urethral abscess, excessive secretion of urates, symptomatic skin disorders.

Jupiter in Sagittarius: Fistula, rheumatism, gout, diseases arising from putrefaction in the blood.

Jupiter in Capricorn: Eczema, obstruction affecting liver function, lipoma. By reflex action into Cancer: jaundice.

Jupiter in Aquarius: Lumbago, milkleg, disorders of the saphenous vein, lymphatic maladies, leukemia (when severely afflicted, with a train of evil directions).

Jupiter in Pisces: Cysts, glandular complications, iatrogenic illnesses, diseases stemming from alcoholism and drug abuse.

THE DISEASES OF SATURN

Writers of the past have, with one accord, regarded Saturn as the worst afflictor among the planets, where human health and happiness are concerned. He has been known as Kronos or Cronos, from which we derive the term chronic as applied to long-term diseases and infirmities. Hence the designation, the Greater Infortune, applied to him.

Saturn afflicts, wherever he is placed in the natal chart, although he can also act as a steadying and much needed restraining influence (as when posited in the restless sign of Gemini).

Just as Mars energizes and tends to burn up or throw out the accumulation of wastes in the body, Saturn, which embodies the opposite principle of restrictions, can inhibit the function of every organ or process in the body.

Saturn's influence is binding, cold, chronic, crystallizing, hardening, depleting, and retarding. He is the author of the aging process in man; of debilities arising from falls or freezing temperatures; skin troubles; tooth decay; and all psychosomatic disorders, brought on through worry, melancholy, and pessimism.

Saturn's pathogenic qualities when placed in each of the twelve zodiacal signs are:

Saturn in Aries: Tooth troubles, head colds, deafness, chills, cerebral anemia, blood clots in blood vessels of the brain.

Saturn in Taurus: Decay of the lower teeth, chronic hoarseness, melancholia, suppurating gums, diphtheria. By reflex into Scorpio: constipation.

Saturn in Gemini: Chronic bronchitis; rheumatism in shoulders, arms, and hands; fibrosis of the lungs; dyspnea; asthma; pulmonary consumption.

Saturn in Cancer: Chronic gastritis, ague, anemia, chlorosis, cancer of the breast, gastric ulcer, abnormal appetite, gallstones, phthisis.

Saturn in Leo: Muscular weakness, curvature of the spine, heart disease, arteriosclerosis.

Saturn in Virgo: Appendicitis, transverse colon, impeded peristalsis, obstruction in the bowels, colitis, intestinal complaints.

Saturn in Libra: Sterility, kidney stones, Bright's disease, suppression of urine, malnutrition.

Saturn in Scorpio: Sterility, palsy, amenorrhea, constipation, hemorrhoids, strangury. By reflex action into Taurus: throat ailments.

Saturn in Sagittarius: Hip fractures in the elderly, sciatica, gout, hardening of the liver.

Saturn in Capricorn: Diseases of the skin, knee injuries, rheumatoid arthritis, erysipelas.

Saturn in Aquarius: Asthenia, herniated disc, sprained ankles, pernicious anemia.

176

Saturn in Pisces: Chronic anxiety, rheumatism, cold feet, bunions, rachitis.

THE DISEASES OF URANUS

Uranus, also known as Herschel, the name of the man who discovered it in 1781, is the planet of the unexpected. Astrologers are agreed that his influence produces sudden and spasdomic changes, both in the lives of individuals and of nations.

It is believed that his rays affect the psychic and mental nature of man more than the physical. However, by causing psychological disturbances and producing behavioral changes, he is indirectly responsible for maladies which arise from emotional upsets.

The individual in whose radical chart Uranus is prominent and afflicted has a tendency to act in haste and repent at leisure. Uranus has his exaltation in Scorpio, the sex sign of the zodiac; and in consequence exerts a marked—and Heindel says an evil—influence over the sex life of those receptive to his lower frequency.

The Uranian type of person is eccentric, brusque, creative, and often a revolutionary.

The pathological effects of a discordant Uranus are still not well understood. When ill-aspected, he is implicated in abrupt and usually deep-seated or incurable diseases, accidents, peculiar ailments that are difficult to diagnose, neuralgia, ruptures, lesions, and abnormal growths.

Uranus in Aries: Shooting pains in the head, neuralgia, peculiar brain affections.

Uranus in Taurus: Injuries to the neck during travel; diminished secretion of pituitary hormones, with resulting disorders such as obesity, genital deficiency, and profuse urination.

Uranus in Gemini: Spasmodic asthma, dry cough, colds

arising from sudden exposure to bad weather; asphyxia (when in the Sixth House).

Uranus in Cancer: Stomach cramps, gas, flatulence, hiccough, hysteria.

Uranus in Leo: Spinal meningitis, polio, valvular heart disease, spasmodic heart action, hypertensive cardiovascular disease.

Uranus in Virgo: Ruptured appendix, abdominal spasm.

Uranus in Libra: Renal spasms, electric shocks, venereal skin rash.

Uranus in Scorpio: Deep-seated venereal diseases, involuntary abortions, difficult parturition, sexual aberrations.

Uranus in Capricorn: Neuralgia, loss of teeth by accident, tetanus.

Uranus in Aquarius: Leg cramps; nervous strain; obscure diseases; nightmares; accidents involving electricity, machinery, x-ray, or lightning.

Uranus in Pisces: Cramps and numbness in the feet as a result of sudden exposure to dampness; claustrophobia, endocrine imbalance, lumbago, gout, intestinal colic.

THE DISEASES OF NEPTUNE

Neptune, the planet of mystery and illusion, discovered in 1846, is still something of an enigma to astrologers. On balance, his influence over the nativity of individuals and nations of today's world seems to be evil. The reason, according to recent writers, is that very few persons of our age are sufficiently evolved to respond to his higher vibrations. It is quite probable, they assert, that the influence of this nebulous, far-out (2,793,000,000 miles from the Sun) planet will be more positive over peoples of the distant future—the so-called Sixth Root Race.

For most people of today, he is the planet of chaos, doubt, and fear; the cause of morbid, weird, and sensuous states of mind; of moral degradation, confusion, and psychic disorientation.

This grim judgment of Neptune seems to be confirmed by recent developments in America and throughout the world. As this is written, Neptune is just emerging from a fourteen-year transit of the zodiacal sign Scorpio, whose negative influence is associated with sexual aberration and rebellion against the moral codes of society.

During that transit, we have witnessed the most devastating assault upon the health and sanity of our people that this country has ever been called upon to endure. The fact that they have endured it—even tolerated it—is further testimony of the insidious Neptunian power to promote laxity in the face of peril; and a baffled or confused approach to reality.

Thus the populace of the world's most advanced nation remained for fourteen years in a trancelike paralysis while an appalling percentage of its youth, mistaking filth for freedom and drug-addiction for "liberation," followed diabolical pied pipers to depravity and oblivion; or were sent to die futile and unheroic deaths in the tropical muck of Southeast Asia.

Most texts say that Neptune exercises an influence over the pineal gland, spinal canal, the mind, and various glands of the body.

The afflictions of Neptune are expressed through the mind and nervous system, giving a tendency to obscure ailments, difficult to diagnose and treat unless the physician or healer is familiar with parapsychology and occultism.

Both Max Heindel and Dr. H. L. Cornell were of the opinion that Neptune's pathogenic qualities are stronger when he is afflicted in the Sixth or Twelfth houses or in the signs of Virgo or Pisces.

Neptune in Aries: Disorders involving the cerebral ventricles, pyromania, myopia, conjunctivitis.

Neptune in Taurus: Accidental suffocation, globus hystericus, polyps on the vocal cords.

Neptune in Gemini: Absent-mindedness, obsessions,

wasting of tissues of the arms, neurosis, phobias, hypermania, sleepwalking.

Neptune in Cancer: Tumors, fungus growths, schizophrenia, alcoholism, drug addiction, danger of drowning.

Neptune in Leo: Weakness in the depressor nerve of the heart, cardiac ailments caused by drug use, depletion of vital fluids, delirium (during illness characterized by high fever), affections of the spinal marrow.

Neptune in Virgo: Hypochondria, food allergies, poisoning, anxiety neurosis, peculiar and rare diseases.

Neptune in Libra: Lesbianism (when square with the moon at birth), venereal dysentery, nervous complaints, lethargy.

Neptune in Scorpio: Passional excesses, sexual perversion, priapism, narcotic addiction, disorders of the thymus gland, birth deformities, epilepsy.

Neptune in Sagittarius: Religious ecstasies, multiple sclerosis, unusual accidents affecting hips and thighs, diseases of the lung tissues.

Neptune in Capricorn: Hypoplasia of the pineal gland, malnutrition, depletion of the vital fluids, skin ailments proceeding from hormonal deficiency, wasting diseases.

Neptune in Aquarius: Functional psychoses, cyclothymic temperament, alcoholism (when in 25° ♒), conversion hysteria.

Neptune in Pisces: Catalepsy, glandular disorders of the feet, plantar warts, fungus infestations, involuntary mediumship.

THE DISEASES OF PLUTO

So far as astrology is concerned, Pluto is a comparative newcomer to the company of celestial dignitaries. Discovered in 1930, the yellowish, distant, little planet has been the subject of controversy to astronomers and astrologers alike.

Astronomers are puzzled, among other things, by its curious and unaccountable orbit. Its elongated course takes it to a distance of over four billion miles from the Sun at its aphelion, then back to within the almost-circular orbit of Neptune at perihelion.

This and other peculiarities which do not fit astronomical theories concerning planets have led some astronomers to suggest that Pluto is really not a planet at all, but a former satellite of Neptune, which escaped when its mother planet lost gravitational mass through evaporation during the early stages of its history.

British astronomer Patrick Moore's description of Pluto vividly conveys the feeling of remoteness, mystery, and sinister quality that perhaps justifies naming it after the Greek god of Hades, the dark and gloomy abode of the dead. He writes:

"The queer little planet is a world of shadowy half-light, moving in solitude around the fringe of the Sun's kingdom—cut off from its fellows, lifeless and utterly alone."

Could such a small, outermost wanderer along the rim of the solar system exert any decisive influence over life on Earth?

Leading astrologers are of one accord in asserting that it does. Several have noted that the date of Pluto's discovery coincided with a period of gangsterism and organized crime in America and with the rise of dictatorship abroad.

Australian astrologer Furze Morrish believes that the outbreak of World War II was due to the entrance of Pluto into the sign of Leo (in 1937).

British astrologer Jeff Mayo agrees with the theory that Pluto is associated with violence and awesome power, and ventures the opinion that it was that planet's influence which was responsible for the Great Depression.

Dr. Regina E. Lorr, an American practitioner of the art, recently expressed the view that, of all the planetary

181

vibrations that have influenced mankind, Pluto appears to be the predominant force for good or evil. In *American Astrology* (February, 1970) she writes: "Pluto is the planet of extremes; he can take us to the heights of success and happiness, or to the depths of failure and despair."

She attributes to Pluto's advent all the wars, assassinations of national leaders, kidnappings, and major upheavals of the past 40 years.

Some of the key words which have been assigned to Pluto are: transformation, annihilation, renewal, death and rebirth, coercion.

There are not yet available sufficient data concerning the physiological effects of Pluto to present in detail a reliable guide to astrodiagnosis. Knowledge comes slowly, based upon years of experience and analysis. Most of the published information regarding the pathogenic qualities of an ill-aspected Pluto represents educated guesswork and extrasensory perception rather than systematically observed fact.

It has been reported, but none too reliably, that Pluto governs the widely discussed nucleic acids, DNA and RNA, which control the body's enzyme patterns, and are being used experimentally in several rejuvenation regimens. Acording to this theory, an afflicted Pluto may produce atypical or "erroneous" molecules of the acids, resulting in premature aging or degenerative diseases.

Whatever the soundness of this judgment, there is empirical evidence, as yet inconclusive, that Pluto, when afflicted, does play a role in such ailments of age as hardening of the arteries, arthritis, chronic acidosis, and senile deterioration in the form of disturbed memory and reduced interest span.

Dr. W. M. Davidson, who regarded Pluto as a kind of supercharged Mars, observed that, when that planet is badly aspected in Gemini, it tends to pneumonia. He also warned that, if Pluto is posited in a fixed sign and afflicting the Sun in a birth map, the native should have constant checkups covering any suspicious lumps in the body, as that configuration predisposes to carcinoma.

There is disagreement among foremost astrologers as to whether Pluto is the ruler of the sign Scorpio or of Aries. Editors of the *Moon Sign Book,* founded by Llewellyn George, favor the Aries connection, reasoning that "Scorpio is more the sign of death and regeneration rather than the death and transformation that is Pluto."

Brotherhood of Light astrologers, on the other hand, believe that Pluto rules the negative, fixed-water sign, Scorpio.

"As Scorpio rules the lower part of the kidneys, as well as the sexual organs," wrote the late Elbert Benjamine, "the kidneys may be affected by an aspect involving Pluto, as well as by an aspect involving Venus or Mars."

The Rosicrucian Fellowship of Oceanside, California, also associates Pluto with the zodiacal Eighth House and holds the view that, when Pluto is placed in the Eighth House of a natal horoscope (and presumably afflicted therein), "it may indicate a mysterious death, possibly through surgery or after disappearance."

The authorities who updated recent editions of Sepharial's *New Dictionary of Astrology* agree with this opinion. They write: "Pluto afflicting the Hyleg [giver of life] or in the 8th House exercises a strange vibration. It can cause total disappearance so that the end of the person or the actual cause of death may never be definitely known. From another standpoint it will show a condition of death where the body is never recovered and where burial is not possible. . . ."

Because of Pluto's extremely slow motion, as compared to those planets nearer to the Sun, his transit of a single zodiacal sign can take anywhere from 13 to 32 years. Consequently, its over-all influence is over a generation rather than just an individual. In delineation of an individual's horoscope, therefore, astrologers base their judgments chiefly upon Pluto's house position and aspects, rather than upon the sign it is in.

STELLAR PATTERNS OF COMMON AILMENTS

DESPITE THE great antiquity of astrology and its usefulness as a key to the mysteries of human life and destiny, the development of precise formulas correlating planetary configurations with specific maladies is still in the inceptive stage.

While some of the greatest physicians of the past used astrology in both the diagnosis and treatment of illness, they left little in the way of exact star maps with which to identify an individual disease entity. Most of the literature consists of generalized observations in the form of aphorisms, or rules of prognosis based upon decumbiture and ensuing critical days as determined by aspects of the moon.

It has been only within the last 40 years that researchers have undertaken systematic studies aimed at establishing a check list of stellar patterns associated with various diseases.

The central problem of these investigations, in addition to ascertaining such patterns, has been to make each of them as accurate and reliable as a physical symptom-complex which characterizes a particular disease in orthodox medical practice.

The findings to date are still tentative; but they have brought astrodiagnosis a long way toward a dependable system of identifying not only the symptoms of a disease, but its focal point, hidden or not.

The information presented in the following pages is derived from both statistical research and empirical experience. Thousands of horoscopes were erected, using data abstracted from hospital records; and countless others formed part of case histories in the files of physicians in private practice.

Some of the leading authorities whose work is digested in this compendium are: Dr. W. J. Tucker of England; Dr. W. M. Davidson; Dr. Howard L. Cornell; Elbert Benjamine and his associates at the Brotherhood of Light; Max Heindel and members of the healing staff at the Rosicrucian Fellowship in Oceanside, California; and several practicing physicians who wish to remain anonymous.

More than one diagnostic configuration is given for some of the diseases listed. This is owing to the fact that the same diseases may be caused by more than one combination of planetary afflictions. In a few instances in which experts do not agree as to the basic significators, the differing opinions are equally represented.

Abdominal Pain (see also Appendicitis, Gallstones, Gastric Ulcer, Ulcers). Pain in the abdomen may be due to any of a number of causes. For that reason, diagnosis —whether by the methods of orthodox medicine or by astrological delineation—is often a difficult task.

The most common kind of abdominal pain is ordinary stomach, usually brought on by dietary indiscretions or by foods which irritate the stomach walls.

Sudden and severe abdominal pains may be due to appendicitis, gall bladder trouble, perforated ulcer in the stomach or duodenum, or to an obstruction of the bowels (especially in children).

Persistent abdominal discomfort is sometimes associated with inflammation of the lungs, to a nervous condition, or to the presence of a tumor.

A careful examination of both natal and progressed charts will usually reveal to the medical astrologer where the trouble lies. In fact, expert astrodiagnosis can often pinpoint the seat of an ailment far more readily than medical procedures that depend upon physical symptoms, which are frequently misleading.

The whole abdominal area is ruled by Virgo and by Sixth House influences. The stomach itself is governed by Cancer. The abdominal muscles are controlled by Mars and are strongly influenced when Mars is in Virgo and afflicted at birth. Virgo's opposite sign, Pisces, may also be implicated by reflex action.

Abortion (involuntary). Involuntary abortion, commonly called miscarriage, involves the expulsion of the fetus before it is sufficiently developed for the infant to live. Statistical studies show that abortions occur most frequently between the eighth and twelfth week after conception. An estimated 235,000 such spontaneous abortions occur each year in the United States.

Causes include infections, injuries, malformations, syphilis, improper nutrition, and high fever.

Dr. Davidson warned that, when there are indications in a woman's nativity that a miscarriage might occur, the native should be advised to avoid taking B-complex vitamins, which seem to overstimulate the pituitary gland, thereby affecting the uterus.

Stellar pattern: Pluto in Cancer at birth, and afflicted in the Fifth House.

According to Dr. H. L. Cornell, miscarriage often occurs when several of the Moon's librations do not return to and cross the central line of impulse at the normal monthly period during gestation, thus causing an unbalanced condition of the fetus.

Abscess. An abscess is a circumscribed cavity anywhere in the body, containing pus. The condition is caused by pus-forming germs such as staphylococci, streptococci, and others. When a large accumulation of pus occurs in the chest or pleural cavities, the ailment is called empyema.

Stellar pattern: An afflicted Jupiter causes abscesses, when afflicted by malefics. Brotherhood of Light research indicates a prominent and usually ill-aspected Mars, Neptune, and Pluto.

Diagnostic configuration: (♃ ☌ ♂) □ ☽

Acidosis. Acidosis is a condition of overacidity resulting from abnormal and excessive production of acid in the body, often accompanied by poor elimination.

The most common symptoms of an acid state are headache, rapid breathing, debility, and a characteristic sweetish odor to the breath.

As diabetes is usually accompanied by acidosis, if the condition persists, the natal chart should be checked for indications of that disease and, when found, medical treatment should be sought.

Stellar pattern: One of the negative planets—Moon, Neptune, Saturn, Venus—is usually prominent and afflicted, often involving an aspect to Jupiter.

Diagnostic configurations: (♃ ☌ ♄) □ ♀; ♂ ☍ ♃

Acne. Acne is a chronic inflammation of the oil glands and hair follicles of the skin. It is characterized by pimples and blackheads and occurs most frequently among boys and girls from puberty to the age of twenty-five.

Various physical causes have been ascribed to the disease. They include glandular dysfunction, overindulgence in stimulants and sugar, certain drugs to which some persons are sensitive, and metabolic disorders.

Stellar pattern: There is generally an ill-dignified Venus in the birth chart, usually afflicted by Mars. Cornell gives also the Sun afflicted in Aries, and states that afflictions in Cardinal signs predispose to acne or other skin troubles. Mars afflicted in Taurus is associated with acne rosacea, a chronic congestion affecting the skin of the face.

Diagnostic configurations: ⊙ □ or ☍ ☽; (♀ ☌ ♄) □ ♂

Adenoids. Enlargement of the lymphoid tissue in the throat and back of the nose is a condition commonly called adenoids. A child whose adenoids have been repeatedly infected and inflamed may suffer from disorders proceeding from their permanent enlargement. He catches colds more easily, and may experience trouble with his hearing, owing to disturbances of the Eustachian tubes.

Stellar pattern: Mars in or afflicting the 24 deg. of Taurus or Scorpio. Less frequently, Libra, when afflicted by the square or opposition of Mars.

Diagnostic configurations: (♄ ☌ ♆) ☍ ♀; ♂ □ ♀

Adhesions. When tissues heal, following surgery or accidental injury, the resulting scars sometimes cause the adjacent areas to adhere to each other. Such adhesions, when they occur after abdominal operations, often cause severe pain because the fibrous scar tissue is not elastic, and will not stretch with bodily movements.

Stellar pattern: There is generally an ill-dignified Venus with an afflicted Saturn in the radix. The parts of the body most likely to be affected are those governed by the sign in which the natal Saturn is posited.

Aging (senescence). Old age is not, per se, a disease, but rather a kind of fatigue—a decline little by little into decrepitude. The body's cells gradually lose their regenerative power, with a resultant toughening of the tissues.

In a sense, the process of aging begins at birth. It is more accelerated at certain ages for some persons than for others, the heredity factor determining to a large extent the age at which onset of physical decline becomes apparent. In some families, the members retain their youthfulness and vigor well into their advanced years. In others, the ravages of time start to manifest in late middle age.

It should be borne in mind that senescence is not the

189

same thing as senility. Whereas senescence is simply the uncomplicated process of growing old, senility is characterized by a variety of pathological conditions. Some of the more common of these are arthritis and rheumatism, hypertension, cardiovascular diseases, enlargement of the prostate in men, hormonal deficiencies, eye troubles, and emotional disturbances.

In astrological delineation, old age and the conditions surrounding the native during his final years are indicated by the Fourth House and its influences, and to a certain extent by the Twelfth House.

Saturn has traditionally been considered the planet of old age, and it is his influence which tends to calcify the tissues and blood vessels, to precipitate mineral deposits in various parts of the body, and to weaken the organs concerned with elimination of wastes from the body.

Among the zodiacal signs, the third decanate of Virgo (September 14 to September 23) governs old age, infirmity, decay, and final dissolution.

According to some authorities, if one or more of the malefics (Neptune, Uranus, Saturn, or Mars) are posited in the Fourth House at birth, near the lower meridian and severely afflicted, the native frequently experiences a sad or unfortunate old age.

The quality called childishness is denoted by Mercury occupying a weak sign at birth, evilly aspected by Saturn.

Alcoholism. A definition of alcoholism that will satisfy all medical experts (or all astrological authorities, for that matter) has yet to be written. There is still considerable disagreement among them as to what characteristics identify a person as an alcoholic.

In the days before the ascendancy of the various psychological disciplines, there was no confusion on this point. If an individual was a drunkard, he was a drunkard; and there were no shades of difference which made him appear in a better light.

For our purposes, let us adopt the common-sense view

190

that an alcoholic is a person who periodically and compulsively drinks to excess, to the degree that he is not able to carry on his normal activities, and is a poor risk for accident insurance.

Most medical astrologers of the past held that alcoholism was a disease primarily of the watery signs—Cancer, Scorpio, or Pisces. Recent studies, however, clearly show that the zodiacal sign is not the major determinant in the development of an addiction to alcohol.

On the other hand, certain *degrees* of the zodiac are involved often enough to be significant. These are 9 deg. and 25 deg. of the Fixed signs (Taurus, Leo, Scorpio, and Aquarius), and 11 deg. of the Cardinal signs (Aries, Cancer, Libra, and Capricorn).

Dr. W. J. Tucker, the English researcher, relates the diseases to a planetary type, by which he evidently means an individual marked by influences of the planet traditionally said to rule the day of the week on which he was born. For example, a person born on Monday would be a Moon-type; if on Tuesday, a Mars-type; and so on.

Tucker reported that his study of the nativities of alcoholics, selected at random from medical archives, indicates that the Mercury-type person—born on Wednesday—is more likely to become addicted to alcohol than individuals born on other days.

It would seem evident, however, that considerable further research is necessary before this theory can merit uncritical acceptance.

Stellar patterns: Neptune ill-aspected and tenanting the Sixth House predisposes the native to both alcohol and drug addiction.

A prominent and afflicted Saturn in the Fifth House (especially if ill-aspected by Neptune in Pisces) inclines the subject to secret indulgence.

Mercury or Mars afflicted in Cancer is also an indication of potential weakness which could manifest during periods of emotional stress or reverses of fortune.

The additional factor of severe affliction to one or both

191

of the Luminaries is also necessary to produce a problem drinker.

Diagnostic configurations: (♂ ☌ ☽) □ Ψ; ⊙ □ Ψ; ☽ □ ☿; ☿ □ Ψ

Amnesia. A partial or total loss of memory is called amnesia. In its most common form, it is attended by an inability to remember words. Morbid changes in brain tissues are usually responsible for the condition.

Stellar patterns: According to Dr. Cornell, the most frequent cause of amnesia is the Sun afflicted in the sign Aries. He also cites the pattern of Mercury holding no aspect or relation to the ascendant.

Diagnostic configuration: (☿ □ ☽) ☍ ♄

Anemia. When there is a sharp reduction in the number of red corpuscles or of red coloring matter in the blood, the condition is known as anemia. It may be caused by a loss of blood through hemorrhaging, or because the production of red blood cells falls below the normal rate, owing to disease or damage in the bone marrow, where the cells are produced.

Stellar patterns: The Sun in Taurus, Leo, or Aquarius, and ill-aspected by the malefics Neptune, Uranus, or Saturn, gives a tendency to anemia. Another pattern is Jupiter in Leo, afflicted by Mars.

Diagnostic configurations: ♂ ☌ ♃; ☿ ☌ ♄

Aneurism. An aneurism is the permanent dilation of the wall of a blood vessel, particularly an artery. The condition is recognizable by the fact that the weak spot in the vessel wall pouches out like a balloon. Aneurisms may be caused by infection, physical injury, or birth defect.

Stellar patterns: The Moon badly aspected by one of the malefics, especially when it is in the zodiacal sign Gemini. The Moon and Jupiter in signs corresponding to the arms, legs, and feet affect the vesicles of these parts, sometimes resulting in aneurisms. An afflicted Leo may also produce aneurisms.

Diagnostic configuration: (☽ ☌ ♃) □ ☿

Apoplexy. The rupture of a blood vessel in the brain is commonly called apoplexy or stroke. Medical texts usually refer to the condition as cerebral hemorrhage or cerebrovascular accident, abbreviated CVA, in the case of strokes.

Stellar patterns: Heindel and others state that apoplexy is one of the pathogenic effects of an afflicted Jupiter, especially when that planet is ill-aspected in Taurus, Scorpio, Aquarius, or Leo. The Sun in Aries, in discordant aspect to Uranus, also gives a tendency to cerebral hemorrhage. The Sun aspected by an ill-dignified Jupiter is another pattern.

Diagnostic configurations: There are a great many formulations denoting a predisposition to cerebral thrombosis. Frequently involved are Venus and Mars, with the Sun (elevated and strong. Typical are: (♂ ☌ ♃) □ ♄; (♀ ☍ ♅) □ ♄; (☽ ☌ ♅) □ ♀, with ☿ □ ♄; (♀ ☌ ♄) □ ♃; (♄ ☌ ♅) □ ♃; (♃ ☌ ♄ ☌ ♅) ☍ ☿; (☿ ☌ ♃) □ ♂ ☍ ♄, when ♀ ☍ ♅.

Appendicitis. Swelling and inflammation of the appendix, a small fingerlike projection from the large bowel, is called appendicitis. The condition results from an infection caused by germs.

Stellar patterns: Mars afflicted in Virgo or Scorpio is a frequent pattern for appendicitis. Uranus is the afflictor most often found in the formulation.

Diagnostic configurations: (☉ ☌ ♃) □ ♂; (♂ □ ♃) ☍ ♅.

Arteriosclerosis. Hardening of the arteries is a familiar term to most laymen. Medically, the condition is called arteriosclerosis. The artery walls lose their elasticity and, when subjected to a sudden increase in blood pressure, may rupture. The exact etiology of arteriosclerosis is not known.

Stellar pattern: Jupiter in Leo or Aquarius and afflicted by Saturn is a frequent index of arteriosclerosis. Heindel says that Saturn in the sign Leo gives a tendency to hardening of the arteries. Saturn conjoined Jupiter in the Sixth House may also denote that condition.

Diagnostic configurations: ♄ ♂ ♃; ♄ ♂ ♃ ♂ ♀; (♄ ♂ ♀) □ ♃; ♀ □ ♃ □ ♅; (♂ ♂ ♃) □ ♆.

Arthritis. The disease known as arthritis involves inflammation of the joints. There are a number of types of arthritis, and an estimated 8,000,000 persons in the United States suffer from the malady, either in a mild or a more severe form. Physical causes include infections, metabolic and digestive disturbances, degeneration of the tissues, nervous disorders, allergies, tumors, and diseases of the bones. At this writing, medical researchers have not found a cure for either rheumatoid or degenerative arthritis.

Stellar pattern: Saturn is the chief malefic agent in the development of arthritis, especially when he is posited in the Sixth House and is ill-aspected by Mars. Orthodox medical practitioners have noted that persons suffering from arthritis also experience depression, a salient characteristic of the Saturn influence.

Diagnostic configurations: (♂ ♂ ♄) □ ♃; ☉ ☍ ♅; (♆ ☍ ♂) □ ♄; (♂ ♂ ♄ ♂ ♀) □ ♆; ☽ □ ♂; (☽ ♂ ☿) ☍ ♃.

Asphyxia. Suffocation resulting in loss of consciousness from too little oxygen and too much carbon dioxide in the blood is called asphyxia.

Stellar patterns: The natal Sun afflicted in the sign Aquarius presages the danger of asphyxia. An ill-dignified Uranus posited in the Sixth House also gives a tendency to spasmodic conditions associated with that misfortune.

Diagnostic configuration: (☉ □ ♆) ☍ ♄.

194

Asthma. As the Greek name for this disease indicates, it is characterized by severe gasping for breath or bronchial spasm. The etiology of all cases is not clearly understood. The condition may be caused by irritation of hypersensitive bronchial tubes, by psychological factors, allergies, infections, tuberculosis, and disorders of the nervous system.

Stellar patterns: The most common stellar patterns associated with asthma involve either an affliction in the sign Gemini or an evil aspect to its ruler, Mercury. Sometimes Sagittarius may be implicated by reflex action to Gemini. Critical degrees of the disease are 18 deg. Gemini or Sagittarius, and 4 deg. Virgo or Pisces.

Other frequent combinations are the Sun square or opposition to the Moon in the common signs; Neptune in Gemini, conjunct Saturn; Uranus afflicted in Gemini; Saturn in Cancer, occidental and ill-aspecting the Sun; and Mars afflicted in Gemini.

Diagnostic configurations: ☿ □ ♅; (☿ ☌ ♂) □ ♅.

Atrophy. The degeneration and death of bodily tissue is called atrophy. The disease may attack any part of the body.

Stellar patterns: Saturn heavily afflicted in the natal chart is the principal indicator. The parts of the body which will probably be affected are those ruled by Saturn at birth and by direction, and those corresponding to the house in which Saturn is positioned.

Diagnostic configuration: (☉ □ ♄) ☍ ☽.

Baldness. Experts who have made extensive studies of the subject report that most forms of baldness are hereditary and limited chiefly to the male. (In the rare cases in which hereditary baldness has affected women, it has been a recessive characteristic—that is, tending to breed out of the successive generations, rather than to multiply.)

Cases of alopecia may also occur as a result of infection, glandular dysfunction, and high fevers.

Stellar patterns: The Sun rising in fiery signs and

afflicted at birth predisposes to premature falling of the hair. The same is true when Saturn or Jupiter is ruler of the ascendant and occidental.

The Moon conjunct the Sun or Mars in Aries, particularly when in the ascendant, inclines to baldness.

Cornell expresses the view that rapid falling out of hair in early life is denoted by Jupiter in Sagittarius, especially if Jupiter is in the ascendant.

Diagnostic configuration: (☊ ☌ ♀) □ ♃.

Barrenness (sterility). Barrenness or sterility is simply the inability to have children. The condition may be temporary or permanent; and either the man or the woman, or both, may be responsible. For that reason, it is necessary to examine the nativities of both to determine the cause and whether it is possible to overcome it.

Stellar patterns: Generally, when the Sun and/or Saturn are in barren signs and exercising rulership over the Fifth or the Eleventh House, there may be difficulty in having children. The good aspects of Jupiter or Venus in the birth map of either marriage partner can modify or obviate this affliction.

Diagnostic configurations: (☉ ☌ ☿) ☍ ♄
(♀ ☌ ♄) □ ☽

Biliousness (see also Cholecystitis and Hepatitis). Laymen refer to liver complaints generally as biliousness, while persons with professional training in medicine prefer to identify the various forms of liver trouble by scientifically exact designations. Frequent causes of biliousness are improper diet, infections, jaundice, and alcoholism.

Stellar patterns: In most cases of liver trouble, Jupiter is prominent and badly aspected. Typical is the combination of the Sun in Cancer, square to Jupiter. Other formulations are the Moon in Virgo, afflicted by Saturn or Uranus; and Neptune, Uranus, or Saturn in Gemini or Scorpio, afflicting the Sun or Moon.

Diagnostic configuration: (♃ ☌ ☽) □ ♄

196

Bladder Ailments. The human bladder is a saclike receptacle in the pelvic cavity, which stores urine flowing from the kidneys. It has a capacity of almost one pint. Morbid conditions of the bladder include inflammation caused by infections, tumors, and bladder stones.

Stellar patterns: Bladder troubles are indicated in the radix by Mars or Pluto in Scorpio and afflicted by a malefic. The Seventh and Eighth houses deserve special scrutiny.

Diagnostic configuration: (♂ ☌ ♄) □ ♇

Blindness. There are many causes of blindness, whether in one or both eyes. In the present résumé, however, we are not concerned with loss of eyesight as a result of accidental injury, but that caused by diseases of or affecting the eye.

Stellar patterns: The natal Sun and Moon with nebulous stars (Pleiades, Ascelli, Antares, Praesepe, Deneb, and Hyades) and aspected by a discordant Mars or Neptune incline to eye troubles. Similarly, the Moon conjunct the Pleiades in the Seventh House and afflicted by Mars gives a tendency to poor eyesight. The Sun in Aries, afflicted by Saturn at birth, predisposes to loss of vision in both eyes.

In the first century, Ptolemy wrote: "The native's sight will be impaired if the Moon be opposed to the Sun, and joined with the nebulous stars; and if the Moon be in the Western angle, and both the malefic stars in the Eastern angle, the Sun being in the angle also, the native will become blind."

According to Hindu astrology, the Sun rules the right eye and the Moon the left eye.

Diagnostic configurations: (☉ ☌ ☽) □ or ☍ ♂
(☉ Sig. ☍ ☽) □ ♆

Blood poisoning. There is no single disease entity called blood poisoning. The term refers to absorption of toxic substances into the blood, irrespective of their source.

Currently, public attention has been forced upon the great number of potentially harmful chemicals we daily ingest with our food. These include fertilizers, insecticides, additives to give supermarket products better appearance or long shelf life, and so on. Any foreign substance in any amount is more or less toxic when it gets into the bloodstream.

Stellar pattern: The principal stellar formulation corresponding to blood poisoning is that of Jupiter in Aquarius, severely afflicted by Mars or Neptune.

Diagnostic configuration: $(\;2\!\!\!+ \; \delta \; \delta\;) \; \square \; \Psi$

Boils. A boil is a skin infection, usually occurring on areas that are covered with hair follicles, which make it easier for germs to penetrate beneath the skin.

Stellar patterns: A frequent combination denoting tendency to boils is Jupiter in Pisces, evilly aspected by Mars. The Sun afflicted in the Sixth House also gives a lowered resistance which is often associated with boils. A discordant Jupiter in Aries or Taurus may provide the receptivity which will result in boils on the face and neck.

Diagnostic configuration: $(\;2\!\!\!+ \; \delta \; \odot\;) \; \square \; \delta$

Bronchitis. When the bronchial tubes become infected or inflamed, the condition is known as bronchitis Any of the germs which infect the respiratory tract and lungs may also infect the bronchial tubes.

Stellar patterns: There are quite a number of stellar patterns denoting a tendency to bronchitis. Some of the more common are: the Sun or Moon posited in the Sixth House in fixed signs and badly aspected; Uranus in Taurus or Gemini and afflicting the Sun, Moon, or ascendant; Saturn in Gemini, Sagittarius, or Pisces; Jupiter in Gemini, afflicted by Mars; and Mercury in Gemini, afflicted by Mars.

Diagnostic configuration: $(\; \female \; \delta \; \hbar\;) \; \square \; \delta$

Burns. While children under 15 years of age account

for almost 40 percent of deaths from burns and scalds in the United States, milder cases of lesion from heat or flame are among the most common forms of accidental injury among persons of all ages. Fatalities result principally from secondary shock to the system, rather than from the burn itself.

Stellar pattern: Mars provides the malefic influence which results in burning and scalding, especially when in the sign of Capricorn in the Sixth House.

Diagnostic configuration: (♂ ☌ ♄) ☍ ♃

Cancer. Owing to the fact that there are many different types of cancer and that scientific studies to date indicate multiple causes rather than a single cause, it has been deemed advisable not to attempt a diagnostic formulation of the disease, which would only be misleading and—in the case of self-diagnosis, detrimental—to the reader.

In the present state of the art, astrology shares the dilemma of medical researchers where cancer is concerned. There is still much to be learned before the mystery will be entirely cleared up. Research is going forward, however, and an accurate planetary configuration designating each kind of malignant tumor will eventually be found.

Meanwhile, preliminary data clearly indicate that there is little or no foundation for the belief of older astrologers that cancer is casually related to the zodiacal sign of the same name.

Carbuncle. Laymen sometimes confuse ordinary boils with carbuncles, which are far more serious, being an infection that involves both the skin and the cellular tissue beneath. Carbuncles are caused by pus-forming germs, which produce an undurated, inflammatory mass.

Stellar pattern: Jupiter afflicted in Taurus may produce carbuncles resulting from dietary indiscretions. Mars ill-aspected in Capricorn also tends to both boils and carbuncles, especially during adolescence.

Diagnostic configuration: ♃ □ ♂

Cataract. When the crystalline lens of the eye is clouded over, gradually diminishing vision, the condition is known as a cataract. Specialists can remove cataracts without injuring the eye in any way.

Stellar patterns: The development of cataracts almost always corresponds to a celestial pattern in which Mars is the malefic agent and the Moon is the planet severely afflicted, especially when the ascendant is in the nebulous parts in aspect to Saturn. Another formulation is Neptune in Aries, in discordant aspect to Saturn.

Diagnostic configuration: (☉ M.C. ☌ ☽) ☐ ♄

Catarrh. The term catarrh is an old-fashioned word used to denote an inflammation of the mucous membrane, especially in the nose and throat.

Stellar patterns: A predisposition to catarrh is usually indicated by the Moon in one of the watery signs at birth, and afflicted by Neptune; or Saturn in Scorpio, badly aspecting Pluto or Neptune. Heindel also gives Saturn in Aries and Venus in Aries.

Diagnostic configuration: (☽ ☌ ♄) ☐ ♃

Chicken Pox. A highly contagious disease of childhood, chicken pox is an infectious, eruptive disease known to doctors as varicella. It is caused by a microscopic, filterable virus.

Stellar pattern: The single most definitive pattern is Mars afflicted in Capricorn.

Diagnostic configuration: ♂ ☐ ♄

Cholecystitis. The medical term for inflammation of the gall bladder is cholecystitis. It is usually caused by disturbances of the body's metabolism, brought on by improper diet.

Stellar pattern: Saturn governs the gall bladder and is implicated in influences causing morbid conditions in that organ. A frequent combination is Saturn in Capricorn, afflicted by Neptune.

Diagnostic configurations: (♄ ☌ ☿) □ ♆;
   ☿ □ ♆
   ☿ ☍ ♆

Cholera. Although cholera is not a serious threat in the United States, it is still one of the more serious epidemic diseases in many parts of the world, especially in Asia. It is an acute intestinal disease, causing severe diarrhea, vomiting, cramps in the muscles, suppression of urine in the kidneys, and complete collapse.

Stellar patterns: Mars usually occupies a prominent place in the natal horoscope, as with Mars in Virgo and severely afflicted. An ill-aspected Mercury in Virgo may also predispose the native to contracting the disease.

Diagnostic configuration: (♂ ☌ ☿) □ ♄

Clairvoyance (involuntary). There are three kinds of clairvoyance, or ability to perceive things not visible to normal sight (e.g., things happening at a distance, spirit forms, the human aura, etc.). These are: (1) natural clairvoyance, occurring as "second sight" and involving no special training on the part of the person possessing it; (2) that which is artificially induced by development under a teacher or through hypnotic suggestion, drugs, and so on; (3) an involuntary form which occurs spontaneously, without the person willing it or even desiring it. The latter kind leads to obsessions and demented states of mind closely resembling insanity.

Stellar patterns: Neptune is the primary agent in all forms of involuntary clairvoyance or mediumship. When Neptune is ruler of the nativity, and afflicted in the Sixth or Twelfth house, there is danger of such obsessive seizures. A train of evil directions from Neptune to the ascendant, Sun, Moon, or Mercury tends to increase the influence.

Diagnostic configuration: ♆ □ or ☍ ♅

Colds. The common cold, which has proven so baffling

to medical science, is believed to be caused by a filterable virus, followed by secondary invaders—toxic organisms which infect the nose, throat and respiratory tract.

Stellar patterns: The sidereal origin of colds is clearly apparent in the fact that they occur in epidemic cycles. Dr. W. J. Tucker found that the outbreaks recurred every 33 weeks, which he noted was the exact interval between each successive adverse aspect between Jupiter and Mars.

Dr. H. L. Cornell was of the opinion that colds are caused by Saturn when that malefic afflicts the Sun or Moon from the watery signs. In the nativity, susceptibility to colds is indicated when the Luminaries are conjoined in Saturn; by the Sun badly aspected in Capricorn; by the Sun in discordant aspect to the Moon; and by the Moon afflicted in Pisces.

Diagnostic configurations: ⊙ ☽ ☌ ♄
⠀⠀⠀⠀⠀⠀⠀⠀⠀⠀♂ ☌ ♃

Colitis. The term colitis refers to an inflammation of the colon, which is that part of the large intestine extending from the caecum to the rectum. Irritation may be caused by improper diet, infections, or psychological factors.

Stellar pattern: Mars in Scorpio adversely aspected by Saturn is a frequent combination associated with colitis.

Diagnostic configuration: (♂ □ ☿) ☍ ♆

Conjunctivitis. Inflammation of the mucous membrane which lines the inner surface of the eyelid is called conjunctivitis. It is commonly caused by germs transmitted by towels, unwashed hands, and contaminated swimming pools.

Stellar pattern: In the natal chart, when the Sun is afflicted in the fiery signs and is conjunct, square, or in opposition to the ascendant by direction, the native will be prone to attacks of conjunctivitis.

Diagnostic configuration: ⊙ □ ♂

Constipation. It has been estimated that people of the United States spend $57,000,000 a year on various remedies for constipation, or infrequent and difficult movement of the bowels. There are two principal physical causes of the disorder. One is weakened motor activity of the larger bowel; the other is dyschezia or improper nerve-muscle coordination.

Stellar patterns: There are several celestial correspondences indicating a tendency to constipation. They are: Saturn, Uranus, or Neptune in Virgo and badly aspecting Sun or Moon; the Sun in Virgo or Capricorn and afflicted by Saturn; Saturn in the ascendant and Scorpio rising at birth.

Diagnostic configuration: ♄ ☍ ☿

Cysts. The word cyst refers to any membranous sac in the body, containing a fluid or semisolid substance. Cysts occur most frequently in subcutaneous tissue and in the glands.

Stellar patterns: For a quick elucidation of cysts, the medical astrologer looks first for an affliction to Jupiter, especially when that planet is in the sign of Pisces or of Scorpio. A breast cyst is commonly indicated by Venus in Cancer in the Sixth House and adversely aspected.

Diagnostic configurations: ♃ ☍ ♆

(♀ ☌ ☽) □ ♇

Deafness. There are varying degrees of deafness or impaired function of the ear. Physically, the causes include infectious diseases, accidents, and hereditary defects.

Stellar patterns: Debility of hearing may be indicated in the birth map by the Sun conjunct Mercury in the sign Gemini and posited in the Twelfth House; also, the Sun, Venus, and Mercury conjoined in Pisces in the Twelfth House and evilly aspected by Saturn, Uranus, or Mars.

Diagnostic configurations: (☽ ☌ ☿) □ ♄

(☉ ☌ ♀ ☌ ☿) or ☍ ♄

203

Diabetes. When a person suffers from the disease known as diabetes, it is because the pancreas fails to perform its function of secreting a substance called insulin, which utilizes the sugar in the body. As a result, there is an excessive flow of urine containing sugar. The disease can be controlled, but to date no outright cure has been found.

Stellar patterns: Astrologically considered, diabetes is a Jupiter disease, especially when that planet is afflicted in Libra, Scorpio, or Aries. Another natal formulation is the Sun or Venus afflicted in Libra.

Diagnostic configurations: ♃ ☍ ♄

(⊙ ☌ ♃) □ ♄

Digestive Troubles. When complaints involving the digestive system occur, they often relate to other and sometimes more serious ailments, and are symptoms rather than individual diseases. The general term dyspepsia is ordinarily used to designate impairment of the digestion, irrespective of cause. Ulcers, arthritis, and gall bladder disease all produce digestive upsets.

Stellar patterns: It is important for the astromedical diagnostician, as it is for the physician, to make a careful examination of the natal and progressed charts with a view to determining the source of indigestion, rather than the immediate and localized symptoms.

As a rule of thumb, persons with the Sun, Moon, or Jupiter afflicted in Cancer or Virgo will suffer at one time or another during their lifetime. When the afflictor is Mars, the trouble is usually acute and brief; when it is Saturn, it tends to be chronic.

Diagnostic configuration: (☽ ☌ ☿) □ ♄

Dropsy. The term used by doctors for this complaint is edema. It means an abnormal swelling or accumulation of fluid in body tissues. The condition is usually noticed first in the legs, around the ankles. It may stem from heart or kidney disorders, allergies, and glandular dysfunction.

Stellar patterns: In most celestial correspondences,

204

either of the Lights—but particularly the Moon—is afflicted in Cancer, Scorpio, Aquarius, or Pisces. Heindel adds the Moon afflicted in Leo.

Diagnostic configuration: (☽ ☌ ♀) □ ♃

Eczema. The medical definition of eczema is "a noninfectious skin disease characterized by inflammation, itching and scaliness, for which a definite cause cannot be established." Some of the suspected agents resulting in the condition are food allergy, exposure to toxic chemicals, and mechanical irritants.

Stellar patterns: The medical astrologer looks first for discordant aspects to Venus in Capricorn. Other patterns which merit close scrutiny are Jupiter in Capricorn in the Sixth House and in bad aspect to Saturn; Jupiter in Capricorn, afflicted by Saturn.

Diagnostic configuration: ♃ ☍ ♄
                          ♀ □ ♅

Emphysema. There are several types of emphysema, a condition in which the cells of the lungs become over-dilated, with an attendant accumulation of air. The normal respiratory function is disturbed.

Stellar patterns: The most common formulation is Uranus in Gemini, ill-aspected by Saturn. A less frequent one is Mercury in Gemini square to Uranus.

Diagnostic configuration: ☿ □ ♅

Enuresis. The scientific term for bedwetting is enuresis. It refers to an involuntary discharge of urine, usually during sleep.

Stellar patterns: Enuresis is influenced chiefly by Mars in Scorpio in opposition to Uranus. A second pattern is Venus in Scorpio, afflicted by Mars.

Diagnostic configuration: (♀ ☌ ♂) □ ♆

Epilepsy. The medical name for epilepsy is cerebral dysrhythmia because the seizures are characterized by a disturbance in the normal rhythm of cells in the brain. Attacks are accompanied by convulsions and, in the case of the more severe form, loss of consciousness.

There are two kinds of epilepsy, distinguished by the severity of the attack. Cases in which symptoms are brief and so mild as to go unnoticed by other persons in the immediate vicinity of the victim are called *petit mal.* A more serious condition is *grand mal,* which is marked by tonic and clonic convulsions.

Stellar patterns: Most experts in medical astrology agree that the influence of Neptune, in evil aspect to other planets, is responsible for epilepsy. Suspicion is directed to the pineal gland (governed by Neptune) as the seat of the malady.

Neptune afflicted in Cancer, and afflicting the hyleg from that place is a typical stellar concurrence. Neptune in the Sixth House and adversely aspecting Mercury is another.

Tucker reports, as a synchronization for *grand mal,* the Sun conjoined Neptune, and Moon conjoined Uranus in opposition to Mercury, square to Mars.

Diagnostic configurations: ♂ ☌ ♆ ☌ ♃

(♄ ☌ ♅ ☌ ☿) □ ♂

(♀ ☌ ♆) ☍ ♄

Petit mal: (♂ ☌ ♅) ☍ ♆

Fistula. A fistula is an abnormal, hollow passage leading from a cavity or organ of the body to the surface. The most common kind occurs near the rectum.

Stellar patterns: A predisposing combination is Sun in Sagittarius, adversely aspected by Saturn or Mars. The Moon in Scorpio conjoined to Saturn is another.

Diagnostic configurations: (☽ ☌ ♂) □ ♄

♀ ☌ ♆

Frigidity. A disturbance of the sexual function in women, characterized by abnormal indifference and absence of gratification, is called frigidity. The condition may be of a temporary nature, or more or less permanent. The seat of the problem may be psychological, or may involve the endocrine glands.

Stellar patterns: In the nativity, the Sun or Moon in Scorpio, conjoined or in evil aspect to Saturn, can produce frigidity, unless other horoscopical components offer contradictory testimony. Cornell states that the Sun by progression making no aspect to natal planets for a long period of time may produce temporary frigidity. Another pattern is the Moon partile to the ascendant.

Diagnostic configuration: (☽ ☌ ♂) □ ♄

Gallstones. Small solids composed of cholesterol, bile pigment, and lime, which sometimes form in the gall bladder and bile duct, are called gallstones. Their presence causes inflammation of the gall bladder and swelling of the gall ducts. When they block the flow of bile, they produce jaundice (q.v.) and a number of associated symptoms.

Stellar patterns: Saturn in Leo, with several planets in Capricorn, indicates a tendency to gallstones. When Leo is on the ascendant, Capricorn falls on the cusp of the Sixth House, a combination which portends trouble with the gall bladder.

Diagnostic configurations: (☉ ☌ ☿) □ ♂
(♃ ☌ ♂) □ ♄

Gastric Ulcer. An ulcer or open sore in the stomach or the intestines is often called a gastric ulcer. Ulcers occur ten times as often in the duodenum—the first section of the small intestine—as they do in the stomach. Because people who develop gastric ulcers usually live tense, stressful lives, it is believed that psychological factors are largely responsible.

Stellar patterns: Saturn in Cancer, square to Jupiter, is a common celestial correspondence of gastric ulcer. Others

207

are Sagittarius in Capricorn, in opposition to the Moon; and Mars in Cancer and afflicted.

Diagnostic configurations: ☿ ☌ ♂
(♃ ☌ ☽) □ ♂
♃ ☌ ♄

Gastritis. The term gastritis refers to inflammation of the stomach. The wall of the stomach becomes red and swollen and, if the inflammation is severe enough, will hemorrhage. Gastritis is caused by irritating substances or toxins, ulcers, digestive disorders, and excessive use of tobacco or alcohol.

Stellar patterns: The Sun conjunct Mars in Cancer gives a tendency to gastritis. Mars in Cancer in the Fourth House predisposes to the same ailment.

Diagnostic configuration: (☉ ☌ ♂) □ ☽

Goiter. Enlargement of the thyroid gland results in a condition known as goiter. It is common in those parts of the world, including some inland areas of the United States, where there is a deficiency of iodine in the food. It is about five times as prevalent among women as among men.

Stellar patterns: The common celestial influences causing goiter are: Venus afflicted in Taurus; and Venus in Taurus in the Sixth House.

Diagnostic configurations: (♃ ☌ ♄) □ ♆
(♀ ☌ ☉) □ ♆

Gonorrhea. The venereal disease known as gonorrhea is characterized by inflammation of the genitals, accompanied by a purulent discharge. It is contagious and is transmitted usually by sexual contact.

Stellar patterns: Salient formulations are: Venus afflicted in Scorpio or Pisces; Venus in the Sixth House and ill-aspected by Mars; the Moon in Scorpio, conjunct or adversely aspecting Saturn; and Venus in Libra, evilly aspected by Mars.

208

Diagnostic configuration: (♀ ♂ ♂) □ ♄

Gout. It was once believed that gout was caused by eating rich foods, and it was known as the rich man's disease. The fact is that it may attack anyone, regardless of his economic status. The disease is marked by a painful swelling and inflammation of the joints, especially of the big toe. It is caused by the accumulation of uric acid in the blood, which combines with salt and is deposited as sodium urate in the joints.

Stellar patterns: The Sun in Taurus, square to Jupiter, often produces gout in the middle years. The Moon afflicted in Sagittarius, and the Moon in Capricorn, in adverse aspect to Mars, also incline to conditions which result in gout.

Diagnostic configuration: ♂ ♂ ☿

Headaches. It is often difficult or impossible to pinpoint the source of a headache, whether from the natal scheme or by medical diagnosis. One reason is that headache is not a disease, but rather the symptom of a disease. Thus, headaches may be due to a variety of often complicated causes. Orthodox medicine has developed many different systems of classifications, the simplest of which enumerates over 200 causes, listed under the headings of mechanical, toxic, and functional.

Stellar patterns: As a general rule, according to Cornell and others, most headaches involve the zodiacal sign Aries, the ascendant, Uranus, and Mars. Mars afflicted in Aries is typical.

Diagnostic configuration: (☉ ♂ ♂) □ ♅

Hemorrhoids. Varicose veins occurring at the lower end of the bowel or anal orifice are called hemorrhoids or piles. There are two kinds—external and internal. Poor circulation due to sedentary habits is the most common cause.

Stellar patterns: Scorpio in the Eighth House and adversely aspected by one of the malefics will provide the groundwork necessary for the development of hemorrhoids. Also, Taurus on the ascendant and afflicted by Mars.

Diagnostic configurations: (☉ ☌ ♃) □ ☽
♀ □ ♆

Hepatitis. Inflammation of the liver is called hepatitis. Infectious hepatitis is caused by a virus.

Stellar patterns: Jupiter in Capricorn, adversely aspected by Mars, is a typical formulation denoting hepatitis. Another is Jupiter in Cancer square Neptune.

Diagnostic configuration: (♂ ☌ ♃ ☌ ♆) □ ☽

Hernia. Rupture is the common term for hernia. The disorder is characterized by the protrusion of an organ, usually a part of the intestine, through a tear in the abdominal wall.

Stellar patterns: Hernia corresponds with a natal concurrence of Venus in Scorpio in the Sixth House and afflicted by Saturn. Also, Mars in Virgo and receiving the evil rays of Saturn.

Diagnostic configuration: (♀ ☌ ♂) □ ♄

Hiccough. Hiccups (the common designation for the affliction) are due to an involuntary contraction of the diaphragm that closes the glottis—a breathing tube from the throat—at the moment of breathing in.

Stellar patterns: The causative agent is Uranus, the planet of spasms. Uranus in Taurus, and afflicted by one of the malefics, is the principal significator in the natus. The moon in Cancer, afflicted by Uranus, may also cause hiccough.

Diagnostic configuration: (♅ ☌ ☽) □ ☿

High Blood Pressure. Hypertension, as high blood pressure is known medically, means increased pressure by the blood upon the vessel walls.

Stellar patterns: Jupiter in Leo square Mars inclines to

hypertension especially if Jupiter is posited in the Sixth House. Venus in Leo, square to Mars, is another correspondence.

Diagnostic configuration: ($\hbar$ ♂ ♃) □ ♂

Homosexuality. Until the recent 14-year transit of Scorpio by Neptune, homosexuality was a problem familiar mostly to police and courts or to psychiatrists, who treated it as a disease. Recent demonstrations, demanding the "civil rights of homosexuals," have, with the willing aid of the communications media, forced the subject upon the public as a whole. Astrology always has (and still does) categorized homosexuality as an abnormality of morbid origin.

Stellar patterns: Neptune in the Seventh House in evil aspect to Uranus may give a contrary sexual instinct. Cornell states that "the Luminaries in female signs, configurated together with Mars and Venus, tend to make men effeminate, lustful, salacious, wanton, and to deviate from the limits of nature; and to make women masculine. . . ."

Neptune on the ascendant, especially when in bad aspect to the Significators, may give a tendency to sexual paraesthesia and perversion. Also, Neptune or Uranus, or both in the signs of Cancer or Libra; the Sun, Uranus, and Mars, all in masculine signs and ill-aspected by Neptune; and the Sun and Moon both in masculine signs, evilly aspected by Mars and Venus, tend to Lesbianism in women.

Diagnostic configurations: (☉ ♂ ☽) □ ♆
(☉ ♂ ♀) □ ♅
(♂ ♂ ♀) □ ♆

Hyperacidity (see Acidosis).

Hysteria. Hysteria is a psychiatric condition whose manifestations include anxiety, excitability, and stimulation of organic disorders. Psychiatry classifies the different forms of hysteria as conversion hysteria, hypochondriasis, neurasthenia, sexual disturbances, and organ neuroses with structural change. The basis for the majority of cases is an emotional disturbance in which an illness or the simulation of an illness seemingly provides a way out of the situation.

Stellar patterns: Afflictions to the Sun in a woman's map give a tendency to hysteria, since the Sun rules the emotional nature in women. The Moon is also sometimes involved. A typical combination is the Sun in the Third House, with Mercury on the cusp, adversely aspected by Uranus. The Moon in Aquarius, conjunct or ill-aspected by Saturn, is another formulation.

Diagnostic configuration: ☉ ☍ ♅
☽ □ or ☍ ☿
☽ ☌ ♄

Insanity. The term insanity has come to be more a legal designation than a scientific one. In common parlance, it designates mental derangement or madness.

Stellar patterns: The three principal planets involved in the pattern of mental derangement are the Moon, Mercury, and Saturn. A tendency to mental enfeeblement is to be suspected if there is no aspect at birth between the Moon and Mercury, provided neither aspects the ascendant and is afflicted by one or more of the malefics. Other typical combinations to be looked for are: in a day nativity—Mercury afflicted by Mars; in a night nativity—Mercury afflicted by Saturn; the Moon, Mercury, and ascendant in no relation to each other and Mercury afflicted by one of the malefics, especially if the affliction is from one of the angles; the ill aspects of Neptune, added to those of Mars and/or Saturn. Neptune afflicted in the Twelfth House may presage obsessions and spirit control. Neptune conjunct Mars in Aries, afflicted by Uranus and in bad aspect to the Moon, tends to produce mental disturbance.

Diagnostic configurations: (☽ ☌ ♅) ⚼ ♄
(☉ ☌ ♃) □ ☍
(☽ ⚼ ♅) □, ☌, ⚼ ♄
(♅ ⚼ ☍) □ ♀
(☽ ☌ ♅) □ ☿
(☽ ⚼ ☍) cum ♅ □ ♃

Itch. Itching occurs in a number of skin diseases. It may be caused by food or drug allergy, fungus infections, sensitivity to heat, insect bites, and nervous disorders.

Stellar patterns: Itching is not a single condition, but a symptom. For that reason, the medical astrologer, while taking note of the celestial influences which produce the condition, will also examine the birth map for other ailments for which itching may be the manifestation. A common stellar pattern is Mars or Venus in Capricorn and afflicted by Saturn. Another is Mars in Gemini in adverse aspect to Uranus.

Diagnostic configuration: (☍ ☌ ☿) □ ♄

Jaundice. The condition known as jaundice or icterus develops when the normal flow of bile through the bile ducts is disturbed, or when the liver does not function properly. Bile circulates in the blood, imparting a yellow color to the skin.

Stellar patterns: Jupiter afflicted in Cancer, Virgo, Capricorn, or Pisces given a tendency to jaundice. Additional combinations are: Mars in Sagittarius, in bad aspect to the Moon or the ascendant; Saturn afflicted in Gemini, Leo, or Capricorn; the Sun or Moon in hostile aspect to Saturn, Uranus, or Neptune, when these planets are in Gemini; and the Moon in Capricorn, and afflicted by Mars at the decumbiture.

Diagnostic configuration: (♃ ☌ ☍ ☌ ♅) □ ♄

Laryngitis. The affliction known as laryngitis is characterized by inflammation of the vocal chords or voice box.

It may be caused by infection, irritation by chemical substances, or excessive use of the voice.

Stellar patterns: As Taurus governs the throat, it is not surprising to find that the pathogenic effects of the malefics, when ill-aspecting a planet in that sign, produce laryngitis. Some of the combinations are: The Moon in Taurus, adversely aspected by Mars; Uranus in Taurus and inimically aspecting the Sun, Moon, or ascendant at birth; Saturn in Taurus in the Sixth House; and Mars in Taurus or Scorpio, and afflicted by the square to Saturn.

Diagnostic configurations: (♅ ☌ ♀) □, ☍ ♄

Leukemia. Leukemia has been called a cancer of the blood, since it is a fatal disease of the bloodmaking tissues, characterized by a sudden and great increase in the number of white blood cells.

Stellar patterns: There is some disagreement among medical astrologers as to the exact planetary influences associated with leukemia. Most concur, however, in the opinion that Jupiter plays an important role in the etiology of the disease because of his rulership of the blood. Thus, Jupiter in Cancer in the Sixth House, and in unfriendly aspect to the Moon, *could* be responsible for providing the stellar background of the ailment. Cornell gave Saturn afflicting the hyleg, as well as Saturn in Virgo in malevolent aspect to the Sun, Moon, or ascendant.

Diagnostic configuration: (♂ ☌ ♃) □ ☽

Lipoma. Fatty or lardaceous tumors are called lipomas. They are usually nonmalignant. They are caused by errors in metabolism.

Stellar pattern: The principal planetary vibration concerned in this disease is Jupiter, especially when he is posited in the Sixth House in hostile aspect to Mars.

Diagnostic configuration: ♃ □ ♂

Low Blood Pressure. Just as high blood pressure is called hypertensive, low blood pressure is known as hypotension, meaning a decrease of force by the blood against the vessel walls as it circulates through the body.

Stellar pattern: A prominent Saturn afflicting Jupiter at birth predisposes the natives to low blood pressure, usually in the latter decades of his life.

Diagnostic configuration: (♃ ☌ ♄) □ ♂

Lumbago. One of the most common complaints doctors in general practice have to treat is that of low back pain, familiarly known as lumbago. There are a great many causes of lumbago, and it is necessary for the medical astrologer to examine the natal chart most carefully to determine the seat of the trouble.

Stellar patterns: Uranus afflicted in Libra gives spasmodic lumbago. The Sun in Taurus and conjunct or ill-aspecting a malefic; the Sun in Aquarius, in incompatible relation to Jupiter; Saturn afflicted in Libra; Mercury in Aries or in Libra and in adverse angle to Mars or Saturn; and Venus in the Seventh House, in unfriendly aspect to Saturn.

Diagnostic configuration: (☉ ☌ ♄) □ ♅

Malaria. Although malaria is one of the oldest diseases known to man, it was not until 1880 that a French army surgeon discovered that it is an infectious malady caused by a protozoan parasite in the blood. The disease is transmitted from one person to another by the female anopheles mosquito.

Stellar patterns: Mars is usually the afflictor in the celestial formulation associated with malaria. When in Leo, Virgo, Sagittarius, or Capricorn, and aspecting a discordant Saturn or Neptune, he becomes the primary agent in causing the trouble.

Diagnostic configuration: (♂ ☌ ♃) ☍ ♄

Mastoiditis. The protruding part of the temporal bone behind the ear is called the mastoid. When an inflammation occurs here, the condition is known as mastoiditis.

Stellar patterns: The Moon and Saturn, both afflicted and in discordant relation to each other, give a tendency to mastoiditis. Saturn in Taurus in the Twelfth House and afflicting the Moon or Mercury gives a predisposition to mastoid abscesses.

Diagnostic configurations: ☌ □ ♄

(♄ ☌ ☽) □ ☌

Measles. While measles is chiefly a childhood disease, it can be transmitted to adults, a fact brought home to the public when an astronaut lost his seat aboard a Moon-bound rocket after being exposed to a child who had the disease. The incidence of measles among children has declined very little in the last three decades. The malady is caused by a microscopic virus which passes from child to child.

Stellar pattern: Measles is a disease caused by Mars and Saturn in concert with Pluto and sometimes Neptune. Cornell states that, if Mars is exactly rising or setting at birth, he may denote a likelihood of the native contracting measles. When transiting Mars comes to a discordant aspect with the ascendant early in life, he causes measles and sometimes scarlatina.

Diagnostic configuration: (♂ ☌ ♀) ☍ ♄

Menopausal Syndrome. The climacteric commonly called change of life, which portends the end of menstruation or reproductive life in women, begins when the Moon in the native's progressed horoscope reaches the sign and degree which places her in opposition to her radical position, on her first course the zodiac after the native's birth.

Menstruation ceases when the Moon by progression reaches her third quarter from her radical place on her second course around the twelve signs.

Stellar patterns: Most of the complaints associated with menopause are of a relatively unimportant nature. Many of the psychological disturbances attributed to the change of life are either exaggerated or proceed from other causes.

216

Menopausal difficulties are denoted chiefly by the Moon conjunct Venus, in antipathetic aspect to one of the malefics. The Moon afflicted in Scorpio or Taurus produces the same result.

Diagnostic configuration: (☽ ☌ ♀) □ ♄

Mumps. The onset of mumps is signaled by a swelling of the partoid gland in front of the ear and a high fever. The disease is caused by viral infection. In about one out of every hundred cases, a further complication occurs, involving the swelling of the sex glands.

Stellar patterns: A common stellar configuration associatcd with mumps is Venus in Taurus in the Sixth House in adverse aspect to the Moon or the ascendant. Saturn, Venus, Neptune, or Mars afflicted in Taurus also presage the possibility of contracting the disease.

Diagnostic configuration: (♂ ☌ ♀) ☍ ☽

Narcotic Addiction. The problem of narcotic addiction, which has grown to monstrous proportions during recent years, especially among the young, has been studied at some length by astrologers, most of whom regard it as the result of the combined influences of a transiting Neptune and aspects involving Saturn. To these influences, I would add the baleful effects of Pluto, which provide thc depraved conditions and antisocial setting of the drug habit. The almost daily apologetics of the media in favor of drug users notwithstanding, the fact is that the typical narcotics addict embraces the habit because he is emotionally immature or unstable and unable to cope with his environment. He is discontented, restless, and confused. Drugs gives him pleasure only in the sense that they offer a tcmporary relief from painful mental processes and induce a fleeting euphoria which is often mistaken for self-confidence and "liberation." *Cannabis sativa* (marijuana) is ruled by Saturn, not by Neptune.

Stellar patterns: There are a great many celestial combinations associated with narcotics addiction, but Neptune is involved with almost all of them. Neptune in any weak sign at birth, especially in Virgo and ill-aspected by Saturn, gives a weakness which could lead to addiction. Neptune in conjunction, square, or opposition with the Sun or Ascendant, often portends ailments arising from drug taking. In the radix, when Neptune is setting in opposition to the Luminaries, there is danger of death from overdose or injudicious use of opiates and narcotics. Other significators in the natal chart are: Neptune in the Sixth House, and afflicted by Saturn or Pluto; Mercury in hostile aspect to Neptune; the Moon afflicted in Pisces (which is ruled by Neptune); lord of the Sixth or Twelfth House in Pisces and severely afflicted; and the Moon in Pisces, square Neptune.

Diagnostic configurations: Ψ □, ☍ ☽
Ψ □, ☍ ♄
Ψ □, ☍ ☉

Nephritis. The term nephritis means simply inflammation of the kidneys. The condition may be acute or chronic, depending upon the cause. However, it is always indicated by the presence of albumin in the urine. The ailment is sometimes called Bright's disease, after the London physician who conducted extensive studies of the disease in the early 1800's.

Stellar patterns: Mars in Libra in unfriendly aspect to Venus; Venus in the Sixth House and afflicted by Mars, Saturn, or Jupiter; and a fixed sign rising, with a number of afflicted planets in fixed signs—all predispose the native to kidney trouble.

Diagnostic configuration: ☽ ☍ ♄

Nervousness. A person who suffers from more or less chronic nervousness finds it difficult to concentrate on any one thing, is jumpy and sometimes irritable. The cause of the condition may be either physical or mental, or both.

Stellar patterns: Mercury in Gemini, in bad aspect to Uranus, is almost certain to denote a nervous person.

Uranus afflicted in Gemini, Sagittarius, or Aquarius also predisposes to an emotionally tense, restless individual.

Diagnostic configurations: ☉ □ ♅
♀ □ ♅

Neurasthenia. Although the term *neurasthenia* means simply nervous exhaustion, it is concerned with a condition that is serious. We refer to continuous nervous fatigue, of course, not to an occasional feeling of exhaustion after a trying day. In their textbook, *Principles of Abnormal Psychology,* Drs. A. H. Maslow and Bela Mittelmann have this to say about neurasthenia:

"Neurasthenic patients are disappointed or discouraged people, people who are living a life that is disappointing to them, doing a job they do not like, or who have problems that weigh heavily on their shoulders. Their self-esteem is low; they have feelings of inadequacy, helplessness, or uselessness. They often feel unimportant and unwanted; and they fear rejection, abandonment, or condemnation because of failure; they want to stop functioning."

Stellar patterns: Uranus in Gemini, square Pluto, or Neptune tends to depletion of nerve force. The Sun in Gemini or Sagittarius and badly aspected by Uranus also predisposes the native to neurasthenia.

Diagnostic configurations: ♆ □ ♀
☽ ☍ ♆

Neuritis. Inflammation of a nerve or group of nerves is known as neuritis. The condition is characterized by extreme tenderness and pain in the area around the affected nerve. Neuritis is caused by various infections, rheumatism, and diabetes.

Stellar patterns: Owing to the fact that neuritis may have any one of several causes, it is necessary for the medical astrologer to examine the natal chart carefully to determine whether the sources of the condition are present.

Typical patterns are: Mercury afflicted by Mars or Uranus; 29 deg. Leo or Aquarius involved in the natus; Mars in Gemini, in malevolent aspect to Uranus; and the bad aspects of Neptune to Mercury.

Diagnostic configuration: (☿ ☌ ♂) □ ♅

Nymphomania. Morbid, uncontrollable sexual desire in the female is called nymphomania. The term was derived from the woodland sprites of mythology, who accosted and seduced males. Psychiatrists attribute the abnormal behavior to compensation for various kinds of fears and frustrations. In some cases, it may be an unconscious attempt at self-degradation; in others, a desperate effort to gain the utmost pleasure and excitement from sex for fear it may suddenly be taken away.

Stellar patterns: A characteristic pattern of nymphomania is the Moon or Venus severely afflicted by Neptune at birth, with a prominent Mars providing the dynamic. Another is: Mars conjunct Venus in Scorpio and afflicted by Uranus.

Diagnostic configurations: (♂ ☌ ♀) □ ♅
(♂ ☌ ♀) □ ♆

Obesity. One of the major concerns of great numbers of persons in our well-nourished society is obesity or overweight. Perhaps it is an oversimplification to say that obesity is caused by a person's inability to adjust his appetite to his body's needs, but in most instances that is basically the case. A less-frequent reason for corpulence may be glandular disturbances. Dr. Richard C. Bates, a specialist in the treatment of alcoholism and heart disease, has stated that obesity is the most important single cause of early death in this country. Actuarial statistics concur.

Stellar patterns: A typical celestial combination is Jupiter in Virgo, posited in the Sixth House and afflicted by Uranus or Mars. Heindel gives also the moon afflicted in Cancer.

Diagnostic configuration: (☽ ☌ ♃) □ ♅

Obsession. Psychiatrists define the word *obsession* as a neurotic reaction characterized by a persistent intrusion of, or inescapable preoccupation with, an idea or emotion. Occultists and many astrologers (as well as some parapsychologists), however, use the term in a quite different sense. For them it means the act of nonphysical forces, agents, or spiritual entities independent and separate from the body, besetting a person or impelling him to action from without. (Obsession is not the same thing as *possession,* a condition in which a discarnate entity actually enters the person and takes over his mental and physical processes.)

The rise in bestial, unmotivated murders and mutilation crimes within the past few years in America has focused the attention of leading astrologers on this subject. Writing in a recent issue of *Horoscope,* Beatrice Epstein observes:

"A little recognized fact in the world of criminology is the possibility of criminal motivation by an entity or psychological force outside of an individual's own consciousness. In numerous newspaper accounts of murders or other types of bodily assault, the attacker has denied knowledge of having committed the crime. Sometimes there is an affirmation of a complete mental blackout, during which time the accused was completely unconscious of his activities. With a severely afflicted Pluto, especially if afflicted by Mars and/or Neptune and the Moon, the credibility of such statements should not be rejected. . . . There is a great deal of documented proof to justify the belief that there are strange psychological influences who roam around trying to find a channel through which to express their evil desires."

Stellar patterns: Uranus ruler of the horoscope and afflicted in Scorpio or Cancer provides a channel for nonphysical forces to act through an individual. A similar danger exists when Neptune is posited in the Twelfth House, with Scorpio on the cusp, and afflicted by Pluto or Uranus. Neptune conjunct Moon in the Eighth House and square to Uranus is another pattern which warns of possible obsession.

Diagnostic configurations: (Ψ ☌ ☽) □ ♇
(Ψ ☌ ♂) □ ♄

Pellagra. Pellagra is a deficiency disease resulting from the absence in the daily diet of certain vitamins and proteins, most important of which is niacin or nicotinic acid, found in vitamin B-complex.

Stellar pattern: Virgo afflicted by Saturn, especially if the evil influence be from the Sixth House.

Diagnostic configuration: ☿ □ ♄

Peritonitis. The membrane lining the abdominal cavity is called the peritoneum. When this lining becomes inflamed, the condition is known as peritonitis. Peritonitis may be caused by germs from the blood or from the appendix. Serious consequences follow, often requiring emergency treatment.

Stellar configurations: The Sun, Moon, or Mars in Virgo, posited in the Sixth House and afflicted by Uranus or Saturn, constitutes the most common formulations.

Diagnostic configuration: ☿ □ ♂

Phlebitis. Inflammation of the lining of small blood vessels or veins is called phlebitis. The disease is caused by a breakdown of the valves in the veins, allowing the blood to accumulate in the legs, causing severe pain.

Stellar pattern: Phlebitis often results when Venus is in Aquarius and ill-aspected by Mars.

Diagnostic configuration: ♂ ☌, □, ☍ . ♀

Pleurisy. The pleura is the serous membrane lining the chest cavity around the lungs. Inflammation of this lining is called pleurisy. The condition is characterized by accumulation of fluid in the chest cavity. When this fluid becomes infected by pus-forming germs, it produces a disease called empyema, which may necessitate surgery.

Stellar patterns: In the natal figure, when the Sun is hyleg and square or in opposition to Jupiter by direction, there will be a tendency to pleurisy. The Moon in Sagittarius, in opposition to Jupiter in Gemini, also gives a predisposition.

Diagnostic configuration: (☽ ☌ ☿) □ ♂

Pneumonia. The disease known as pneumonia is usually produced by the pneumococcus germ, of which there are thirty-four different types. Symptoms include fever, prostration, painful breathing, delirium, and sometimes vomiting.

Stellar patterns: Pluto in bad aspect to the Sun in Gemini gives a tendency to pneumonia. The Sun, Moon, or Saturn in Pisces and afflicted by Uranus predisposes to the disease from wet feet or residing in a damp climate, especially if these planets are conjunct Mars in the Twelfth House. Another pattern for the same disease is the Sun in Pisces square to the Moon in Sagittarius.

Diagnostic configurations: ☽ ☌ ♅ ☌ ♂

(☽ ☌ ♆) □ ♄

Prostate Trouble. The prostate is a glandular organ surrounding the neck of the urinary bladder in the human male. It is subject to infection, and to enlargement in some men with advancing years.

Stellar patterns: The most common stellar formulations signaling prostate trouble are: the Sun in Scorpio in evil aspect to Scorpio; the Sun conjunct Saturn in Libra; and Neptune in Scorpio, square or opposition to Saturn.

Diagnostic configuration: (☉ ☌ ♄) □ ♂ or ♇

Psoriasis. A chronic inflammatory skin disease, psoriasis is noninfectious and of unknown origin. Although viruses and germs have been suspected, none has been identified as definitely causing the disease. Some dermatologists have theorized that the condition might be due to the body's inability to metabolize fats.

Stellar pattern: Venus or Mars in Capricorn, afflicted by Neptune, is believed to give a tendency to psoriasis. However, much work remains to be done on this correspondence.

Diagnostic configuration: (♂ ☌ ☿) ☍ ♄

Rheumatism (see section *Arthritis*).

Sciatica. Sciatic neuritis or sciatica is neuralgia of the sciatic nerve, the longest nerve in the body, which proceeds from the lower part of the spinal column, down the thigh, into the leg.

Stellar patterns: The Sun in Sagittarius (or in Gemini by reflex) and afflicted by Uranus, gives a tendency to sciatica. Other predisposing patterns are: Mars in Sagittarius in the Sixth House, afflicted by Uranus; and the Sun or Moon afflicted by Saturn in Libra or Sagittarius.

Diagnostic configuration: (☉ ☌ ☿) □ ♅

Sinusitis. The sinuses are two irregular cavities in the frontal bones of the head, which communicate with the nose through small openings. When germs infect the membrane lining the cavity walls and the opening into the nose is closed, headache and fever result.

Stellar patterns: Moon in Taurus, square to Mars, often predisposes the native to sinus troubles. Also, Moon in Scorpio in opposition to Saturn.

Diagnostic configuration: (♄ ☌ ♃) □ ♂

Sleepwalking (somnambulism). According to psychiatrists, when a person is given to sleepwalking, it is because he is trying to carry out some unconscious desire, which he suppresses during the waking state. The condition appears most frequently during adolescence and involves some kind of personality disturbance.

Stellar patterns: Celestial influences associated with sleepwalking so far observed include the following configurations: the Moon posited in the First House and unfavorably aspected by Neptune at birth or by direction; the Moon rising at birth and afflicted by Neptune; Mercury in discordant aspect to Neptune in the birth figure.

Diagnostic configuration: ☽ □ ♆

Smallpox. Since the discovery of smallpox vaccine by Dr. Edward Jenner in the late 1700's, the incidence of smallpox has declined in most civilized countries to a point where it is largely under control. Occasional outbreaks do occur, however; and, even in the United States, there are areas, where vaccination is not compulsory, that experience epidemics. Smallpox is an acute, virus-caused disease characterized by fever and pustular eruptions, which leave pitted scars on the face.

Stellar patterns: Mars in Taurus in the Sixth House and in hostile aspect to Saturn, especially if Mars is exactly rising or setting at birth, gives a predisposition to contracting the disease. Some researchers have also noted that, when an afflicted Mars is in the ascendant, he seems to precipitate the malady when he reaches a conjunction with the rising degree at birth.

Diagnostic configuratilon: (♂ ☌ ♀) □ ♅

Suicide. Suicide, the taking of one's own life, is an act that is shocking and repugnant to the well-adjusted, normal individual—at least in Western society. The self-immolation of Buddhist monks in Vietnam at one period of the Southeast Asia conflict, however, was a reminder that this attitude is not necessarily a universal one. Hara-kiri in Japan is another example. Even among certain coteries of European society, suicide has traditionally been chosen as an alternative to disgrace. In Sweden, where the suicide rate is unusually high, boredom seems to be the principal motivating factor.

Psychological studies have shown that, before the act of intentional self-destruction takes place, there is a steadily mounting line of emotional intensity directed to that end (similar to an evil train of directions in astrology). It is here that a competent astrologer can help prevent suicides by noting the tendency in the natal figure and progressing it to the culminating point.

According to the various authorities who have conscientiously researched the subject, there is no single suicide configuration. Even the benefics can be instrumental in providing a background of celestial influence which may lead to that tragic end, when such planets come under heavy afflictions from the malefics.

Stellar patterns: General patterns which may incline to self-destruction are: Saturn in Virgo, afflicted in the Fourth House; Saturn conjunct or ill-aspecting the ascendant; Saturn in the Eighth House, with Capricorn on the ascendant and afflicted; Saturn and Mars in Gemini, square the Moon.

Mars in Gemini, Virgo, Aquarius, or Sagittarius, in square or opposition to the Sun or Moon and unfavorably conditioned; Mars conjunct the Luminaries in the Third or Ninth House and afflicted by Saturn, and hostile to the hyleg by direction.

Uranus in Pisces, inharmoniously aspected by Saturn; the transit of Uranus through the Third or the Ninth House, if he afflicted these houses at birth; Uranus evilly aspected in the Eighth House.

Neptune severely afflicted in Scorpio; Neptune in the 16 deg. of the cardinal signs and in discordant aspect to Mercury; Neptune in the Eighth House and square to Saturn.

Mercury in the Sixth House and afflicted by Uranus, Saturn, or Mars; Mercury in the Eighth House, afflicted by the malefics, especially Saturn and Neptune; Mercury conjunct the Moon in fixed signs and adversely aspected by the malefics.

Venus can lead to suicides caused by jealousy, unrequited love, and involvements with the opposite sex: Venus in the Seventh House conjunct Mars and square to Saturn is a typical formulation.

Jupiter provides the emotional background for suicide

226

through financial reverses, bankruptcy, and loss of an estate. Jupiter conjunct Saturn in the Second House, and afflicted by Uranus, is characteristic.

The Moon, when afflicted by Uranus at birth and by direction, especially if she be posited in the Seventh House, leads to suicides motivated by intrigue with the opposite sex.

The Sun, conjunct the Moon and one or more malefics in the Eighth House, tends to suicide through sudden anger or excitement. When other testimonies concur, the Sun and Moon conjunct Saturn or Mars in the M.C. is believed to incline the native to commit suicide to avoid public execution.

Diagnostic configurations: ♀ ☌ ♄ ☌ ♃
♂ ☌ ♅
♃ ☌ ♄

Sunstroke. The harmful effects produced upon the central nervous system and, in consequence, upon the organs of the body by overexposure to the Sun are known as sunstroke. The symptoms of the sickness, which stem from a disturbance of the body's heat-regulating mechanism, include dizziness, headache, and nausea, followed by drowsiness, fever, and often unconsciousness.

Stellar pattern: The stellar influence most often associated with sunstroke is the Sun or Mars in Aries, afflicted by Neptune.

Diagnostic configuration: (☉ ☌ ♂) □ ♅

Syphilis. It is generally believed by medical historians that the disease we know as syphilis was introduced into Europe by sailors returning to Spain with Christopher Columbus from his first voyage to the New World. A Barcelona physician who first described the malady referred to its as the "Disease of the Island of Espanola." The latter was the Spanish name for the island now occupied by Haiti and the Dominican Republic. The name syphilis was derived from a poem by a nobleman of Verona named Fracastorius in 1530.

Syphilis is an infectious venereal disease caused by a spiral-shaped germ called *Spircheta pallida*. One of the most insidious diseases to which man is heir, when the germ invades the body, it multiplies rapidly and spreads throughout the body, gradually permeating every organ. It can be hereditary; and, among certain groups in our society, syphilis is a leading cause of stillbirths.

Stellar patterns: Persons born with the Moon in the Sixth House and afflicted by Venus in discordant aspect from Scorpio may contract syphilis. Uranus in Libra square to Venus in Scorpio is another pattern which predisposes the native to venereal infections.

Diagnostic configuration: (☽ ☌ ♀) □ ♂

Tooth Problems. Saturn governs the teeth, and plays a decisive role in all tooth trouble, whether it be tooth decay, dental defects, or accidental loss of teeth.

Stellar patterns: When, in the natus, Saturn is in Leo and square the Sun, both being in fixed signs, there exists a tendency to defective teeth. Saturn in Aries, badly aspected, gives decay of the upper teeth; and in Taurus, decay of the lower. As a general rule, Saturn in Pisces, afflicted by Uranus, tends to bad teeth.

Diagnostic configuration: ♄ □, ☍ ☉

Tuberculosis. Even though the discovery of antibiotic drugs has drastically reduced the incidence of tuberculosis in America, it is still high on the list of killers. Although it frequently attacks children, it may be contracted at any period in life. The disease is caused by germs called tubercule bacilli. The most frequent seat of the ailment is the lungs, but other organs are also usually involved. It may affect the lymph glands, intestines, larynx, bones, kidneys, superrenals, skin, and generative organs.

Stellar patterns: According to Max Heindel, Saturn in Gemini gives a tendency to tuberculosis, especially if in discordant aspect to another malefic. The Sun conjunct

Saturn in Gemini or in Sagittarius predisposes to this disease.

Diagnostic configuration: ☉ ☌ ♄ ☌ ☿

Tumor (nonmalignant). The term tumor is used to designate any swelling or overgrowth of tissue, independent of its surrounding structures. Benign tumors are those which do not spread throughout the body, and which do not recur when they are removed by surgery.

Stellar patterns: Fibrous tumors usually involve Saturn in unfriendly aspect to Jupiter, especially when the latter planet occupies the Sixth House with a watery sign on the cusp. Fatty tumors are the work of Mars in hostile angle to Jupiter, when the latter is in the Sixth House in the sign of Capricorn.

Diagnostic configurations: ♄ □ ♃
          ♂ □ ♃

Typhoid Fever. Typhoid fever is an acute, infectious disease caused by the typhoid bacillus. It is usually acquired from infected food or water, and is marked by high fever, headache, chills, intestinal disorders, and pains throughout the body.

Stellar patterns: Generally, typhoid fever is a Virgo disease, caused by a planet severely afflicted in that sign, especially if the planet be in the Sixth House of the natal horoscope. Mars afflicted in Cancer in the Sixth House may also presage that malady, if the native is exposed to it. Some authorities also add Mercury in Virgo, unfavorably aspected by Mars.

Diagnostic configuration: ♃ □ ♄ —cum— ♂ ☌ ♀

Ulcers. The term ulcer is understood to mean any open sore other than that caused by an injury. Ulcers are usually caused by infection, damage to the nerves, and, especially in the case of duodenal ulcers, from psychological factors.

Stellar patterns: Saturn, Mars, Uranus, or Pluto in Cancer and afflicting the Sun or Moon therefrom may be considered an ulcer configuration. Another combination is Saturn conjunct Jupiter in Virgo and badly aspecting the Sun, with Uranus in Gemini. Planets in Pisces and in Cancer often warn of ulcers if Neptune or Pluto is prominent and afflicted.

Diagnostic configurations: (☿ ☌ ♂) ☍ ♄

(♂ ☌ ♄) □ ♅

Varicose Veins. Abnormally enlarged, swollen, or knotted blood vessels are known as varicose veins. The condition occurs first in the legs, but may occur at the lower end of the bowel as hemorrhoids.

Stellar patterns: Saturn, Mars, Uranus, or Pluto in Cancer and the Sixth House, inclines the native to varicose veins. (See also the sections on Hemorrhoids and Phlebitis.)

Diagnostic configuration: ♀ □ ♂

Whooping Cough. The medical name for whooping cough is pertussis. It is an acute, infectious disease, mostly of childhood, characterized by a convulsive cough. Sometimes nausea and vomiting will follow the spasmodic coughing fit.

Stellar pattern: Mercury afflicted at birth, with Gemini on the cusp of the Sixth House, is the general pattern of whooping cough.

Diagnostic configuration: (♀ ☌ ♄) □ ♇

Yellow Fever. Yellow fever is an infectious tropical disease caused by a filterable virus which is transmitted by the bite of a mosquito. Symptoms include a high fever and the presence of albumen in the urine. The pulse is feeble and the skin turns a lemon-yellow tint. The body temperature falls below normal. An effective vaccination against the disease is now a widely practiced public health measure, and it is only in areas where vaccination and mosquito abatement programs are not enforced that there is serious danger of contracting the disease.

Stellar pattern: Mars in Leo, afflicted by Saturn or

Pluto, provides the celestial influence favorable to becoming infected with yellow fever.

Diagnostic configuration: (♂ ☌ ♆) ☍ ♄

APPENDIX I

Zodiacal Symbols and Associations

NAME	SYMBOL	RULER	OPPOSITE	ELEMENT	CATEGORY
Aries	♈	Mars ♂	Libra	Fiery	Cardinal
Taurus	♉	Venus ♀	Scorpio	Earthy	Fixed
Gemini	♊	Mercury ☿	Sagittary	Airy	Mutable
Cancer	♋	Moon ☽	Capricorn	Watery	Cardinal
Leo	♌	Sun ☉	Aquarius	Fiery	Fixed
Virgo	♍	Mercury ☿	Pisces	Earthy	Mutable
Libra	♎	Venus ♀	Aries	Airy	Cardinal
Scorpio	♏	Mars ♂	Taurus	Watery	Fixed
Sagittarius	♐	Jupiter ♃	Gemini	Fiery	Mutable
Capricorn	♑	Saturn ♄	Cancer	Earthy	Cardinal
Aquarius	♒	Uranus ♅	Leo	Airy	Fixed
Pisces	♓	Neptune ♆	Virgo	Watery	Mutable

THE ASPECTS

NAME	SYMBOL	DEGREES APART	EFFECTIVE FROM	TO
Conjunction	☌	0	+10°	+6°
Semi-Sextile	⚺			
Semi-Square	∠	45	42°	49°
Sextile	✶	60	56°	63°
Square	□	90	84°	94°
Trine	△	120	113°	125°
Sesquiquadrate	⚼	135	132°	137°
Quincunx	⚻	150	148°	151°
Opposition	☍	180	170°	186°

232

APPENDIX II

Planetary Dignities and Debilities

PLANET	RULES	DETRIMENT	EXALTATION	FALL
☉ Sun	♌	♒	♈	♎
☽ Moon	♋	♑	♉	♏
☿ Mercury	♊ ♍	♐ ♓	♒	♌
♀ Venus	♉ ♎	♏ ♈	♓	♍
♂ Mars	♈ ♏	♎ ♉	♑	♋
♃ Jupiter	♓ ♐	♍ ♊	♋	♑
♄ Saturn	♑ ♒	♋ ♌	♎	♈
♅ Uranus	♒	♌	♏	♉
♆ Neptune	♓	♍	♋	♑
♇ Pluto	♏	♉	♈	♎

APPENDIX III

Table of Sun-Sign Correspondences

SIGN	CELL-SALT	HERBS	VITAMINS	MINERALS
♈	Potassium phosphate	Mustard, aloes, garlic, capers	A, B$_1$, C	Organic iron
♉	Sulphate of soda	Elder, sage, sorrel	A and E	Copper
♊	Potassium chloride	Celery, hops, valerian	B-Complex, C, E, D	Mercury (external use)
♋	Calcium fluoride	Rosemary, watercress	B$_2$, C, E	Fluoride of lime
♌	Magnesium phosphate	Juniper, rue, parsley, dill	C and E	Gold
♍	Potassium sulphate	Summer savory, endive	B-Complex	Zinc (trace amounts)
♎	Sodium phosphate	Thyme, violet, balm	A and E	Manganese
♏	Calcium sulphate	Wormwood, basil	B-Complex, C, E	Iron
♐	Silica	Red clover, sage, mallows	Cholin, C, E	Tin
♑	Calcium phosphate	Red beet, mullein	A, C, E	Lead
♒	Sodium chloride	Tansy, sea holly, comfrey	C and E	Lodestone
♓	Phosphate of iron	Moss, borage, seaweed	E, D, C	Organic iodine

APPENDIX IV Astromedical Connotations

SIGN	RELATED TO:	AFFLICTIONS	DIETARY NEEDS
♈	Head, face, brain, upper jaw, eyes.	Sinus, headache, rhinitis, strokes, fevers, eye troubles.	Beets, celery, carrots, spinach, dates, walnuts.
♉	Throat, neck, Eustachian tubes, cervical vertebrae.	Asthma, goiter, throat ailments, circulatory troubles.	Seafoods, chard, cabbage, onions, beets, pumpkin.
♊	Shoulders, arms, lungs, bronchi, nervous system.	Bronchitis, asthma, nervous disorders, pneumonia, TB.	Lean meat, nuts, celery, corn, apricots, cheeses.
♋	Stomach, breasts, epigastric region, blood serum, womb.	Gastritis, ulcers, dropsy, sclerosis, dyspepsia, tumors.	Milk, kale, watercress, lemons, raisins, rye bread.
♌	Heart, gall bladder, dorsal region of back and spine.	Heart disease, aneurysm, angina pectoris, back pains.	Citrus fruits, eggs, seafood, lettuce, blueberries.
♍	Abdominal area, intestinal canal, pylorus, bowels.	Peritonitis, constipation, intestinal disorders, ileitis.	Protein foods, oats, rye, endive, almonds, chicory.
♎	Kidneys, loins, adrenals, lumbar region, ureters.	Lumbago, nephritis, renal calculi, diabetes, uremia.	Brown rice, fish, eggs, greens, figs, citrus fruits.
♏	Generative organs, bladder, rectum, excretory system.	Fistula, diseases of the genitals, piles, hepatitis.	Asparagus, leeks, radishes, prunes, citrus fruits.
♐	Hips, thighs, coccygeal vertebrae, sciatic nerve.	Locomotor, ataxia, sciatica, rheumatism, hip diseases.	Carrot greens, liver, rice bran, parsnips. Scotch oats.
♑	Knees, skeleton, skin, joints, teeth, right ear.	Broken bones, arthritis, deafness, acne, loss of teeth.	Yogurt, lentils, eggs, broccoli, citrus fruits.
♒	Ankles, wrists, bones of lower limbs, saphenous vein.	Varicose veins, nervous disorders, swollen ankles.	Honey, lemons, apples, hard cheese, turnip greens.
♓	Feet, body's fluids, pineal gland, fibrin of the blood.	Bunions, gout, tumors, fungus, septic poisoning.	Cucumbers, lima beans, beef liver, almonds.

APPENDIX V   Table of Ascendants

The ascendants or rising signs given in the following table are computed for 40 deg. North latitude, but are correct for any birthplace between 25 deg. and 55 deg. N., which includes all of the United States and the southern portion of Canada. Births occurring at midnight or at noon will be read as 12:01 a.m. and 12:01 p.m.

JANUARY 1

A.M.	P.M.
12:01 Libra	12:01 Aries
1:00 Libra	1:00 Taurus
2:00 Scorpio	2:00 Taurus
3:00 Scorpio	3:00 Gemini
4:00 Scorpio	4:00 Gemini
5:00 Sagittarius	5:00 Cancer
6:00 Sagittarius	6:00 Cancer
7:00 Capricorn	7:00 Leo
8:00 Capricorn	8:00 Leo
9:00 Aquarius	9:00 Virgo
10:00 Aquarius	10:00 Virgo
11:00 Pisces	11:00 Virgo

JANUARY 10

A.M.	P.M.
12:01 Libra	12:01 Aries
1:00 Libra	1:00 Taurus
2:00 Scorpio	2:00 Gemini
3:00 Scorpio	3:00 Gemini
4:00 Sagittarius	4:00 Cancer
5:00 Sagittarius	5:00 Cancer
6:00 Sagittarius	6:00 Leo
7:00 Capricorn	7:00 Leo
8:00 Capricorn	8:00 Leo
9:00 Aquarius	9:00 Virgo
10:00 Pisces	10:00 Virgo
11:00 Aries	11:00 Libra

JANUARY 5

A.M.	P.M.
12:01 Libra	12:01 Aries
1:00 Libra	1:00 Taurus
2:00 Scorpio	2:00 Gemini
3:00 Scorpio	3:00 Gemini
4:00 Scorpio	4:00 Cancer
5:00 Sagittarius	5:00 Cancer
6:00 Sagittarius	6:00 Cancer
7:00 Capricorn	7:00 Leo
8:00 Capricorn	8:00 Leo
9:00 Aquarius	9:00 Virgo
10:00 Pisces	10:00 Virgo
11:00 Pisces	11:00 Virgo

JANUARY 15

A.M.	P.M.
12:01 Libra	12:01 Taurus
1:00 Scorpio	1:00 Taurus
2:00 Scorpio	2:00 Gemini
3:00 Scorpio	3:00 Gemini
4:00 Sagittarius	4:00 Cancer
5:00 Sagittarius	5:00 Cancer
6:00 Capricorn	6:00 Leo
7:00 Capricorn	7:00 Leo
8:00 Aquarius	8:00 Virgo
9:00 Aquarius	9:00 Virgo
10:00 Pisces	10:00 Virgo
11:00 Aries	11:00 Libra

JANUARY 20

A.M.	P.M.
12:01 Libra	12:01 Taurus
1:00 Scorpio	1:00 Gemini
2:00 Scorpio	2:00 Gemini
3:00 Scorpio	3:00 Cancer
4:00 Sagittarius	4:00 Cancer
5:00 Sagittarius	5:00 Cancer
6:00 Capricorn	6:00 Leo
7:00 Capricorn	7:00 Leo
8:00 Aquarius	8:00 Virgo
9:00 Pisces	9:00 Virgo
10:00 Pisces	10:00 Virgo
11:00 Aries	11:00 Libra

JANUARY 25

A.M.	P.M.
12:01 Scorpio	12:01 Taurus
1:00 Scorpio	1:00 Gemini
2:00 Scorpio	2:00 Gemini
3:00 Sagittarius	3:00 Cancer
4:00 Sagittarius	4:00 Cancer
5:00 Sagittarius	5:00 Leo
6:00 Capricorn	6:00 Leo
7:00 Capricorn	7:00 Leo
8:00 Aquarius	8:00 Virgo
9:00 Pisces	9:00 Virgo
10:00 Aries	10:00 Libra
11:00 Aries	11:00 Libra

JANUARY 30

A.M.	P.M.
12:01 Scorpio	12:01 Taurus
1:00 Scorpio	1:00 Gemini
2:00 Scorpio	2:00 Gemini
3:00 Sagittarius	3:00 Cancer
4:00 Sagittarius	4:00 Cancer
5:00 Capricorn	5:00 Leo
6:00 Capricorn	6:00 Leo
7:00 Aquarius	7:00 Virgo
8:00 Aquarius	8:00 Virgo
9:00 Pisces	9:00 Virgo
10:00 Aries	10:00 Libra
11:00 Taurus	11:00 Libra

FEBRUARY 5

A.M.	P.M.
12:01 Scorpio	12:01 Gemini
1:00 Scorpio	1:00 Gemini
2:00 Sagittarius	2:00 Cancer
3:00 Sagittarius	3:00 Cancer
4:00 Sagittarius	4:00 Cancer
5:00 Capricorn	5:00 Leo
6:00 Capricorn	6:00 Leo
7:00 Aquarius	7:00 Virgo
8:00 Pisces	8:00 Virgo
9:00 Pisces	9:00 Virgo
10:00 Aries	10:00 Libra
11:00 Aries	11:00 Libra

FEBRUARY 10

A.M.	P.M.
12:01 Scorpio	12:01 Gemini
1:00 Scorpio	1:00 Gemini
2:00 Sagittarius	2:00 Cancer
3:00 Sagittarius	3:00 Cancer
4:00 Sagittarius	4:00 Leo
5:00 Capricorn	5:00 Leo
6:00 Capricorn	6:00 Leo
7:00 Aquarius	7:00 Virgo
8:00 Pisces	8:00 Virgo
9:00 Aries	9:00 Libra
10:00 Aries	10:00 Libra
11:00 Taurus	11:00 Libra

FEBRUARY 15

A.M.	P.M.
12:01 Scorpio	12:01 Gemini
1:00 Scorpio	1:00 Gemini
2:00 Sagittarius	2:00 Cancer
3:00 Sagittarius	3:00 Cancer
4:00 Capricorn	4:00 Leo
5:00 Capricorn	5:00 Leo
6:00 Aquarius	6:00 Virgo
7:00 Aquarius	7:00 Virgo
8:00 Pisces	8:00 Virgo
9:00 Aries	9:00 Libra
10:00 Taurus	10:00 Libra
11:00 Taurus	11:00 Scorpio

FEBRUARY 20

A.M.	P.M.
12:01 Scorpio	12:01 Gemini
1:00 Sagittarius	1:00 Cancer
2:00 Sagittarius	2:00 Cancer
3:00 Sagittarius	3:00 Leo
4:00 Capricorn	4:00 Leo
5:00 Capricorn	5:00 Leo
6:00 Aquarius	6:00 Virgo
7:00 Pisces	7:00 Virgo
8:00 Aries	8:00 Libra
9:00 Aries	9:00 Libra
10:00 Taurus	10:00 Libra
11:00 Gemini	11:00 Scorpio

MARCH 7

A.M.	P.M.
12:01 Sagittarius	12:01 Cancer
1:00 Sagittarius	1:00 Cancer
2:00 Sagittarius	2:00 Cancer
3:00 Capricorn	3:00 Leo
4:00 Capricorn	4:00 Leo
5:00 Aquarius	5:00 Virgo
6:00 Pisces	6:00 Virgo
7:00 Pisces	7:00 Virgo
8:00 Aries	8:00 Libra
9:00 Taurus	9:00 Libra
10:00 Gemini	10:00 Scorpio
11:00 Gemini	11:00 Scorpio

FEBRUARY 25

A.M.	P.M.
12:01 Scorpio	12:01 Gemini
1:00 Sagittarius	1:00 Cancer
2:00 Sagittarius	2:00 Cancer
3:00 Capricorn	3:00 Leo
4:00 Capricorn	4:00 Leo
5:00 Aquarius	5:00 Leo
6:00 Aquarius	6:00 Virgo
7:00 Pisces	7:00 Virgo
8:00 Aries	8:00 Libra
9:00 Taurus	9:00 Libra
10:00 Taurus	10:00 Libra
11:00 Gemini	11:00 Scorpio

MARCH 12

A.M.	P.M.
12:01 Sagittarius	12:01 Cancer
1:00 Sagittarius	1:00 Cancer
2:00 Capricorn	2:00 Leo
3:00 Capricorn	3:00 Leo
4:00 Aquarius	4:00 Leo
5:00 Aquarius	5:00 Virgo
6:00 Pisces	6:00 Virgo
7:00 Aries	7:00 Libra
8:00 Taurus	8:00 Libra
9:00 Taurus	9:00 Libra
10:00 Gemini	10:00 Scorpio
11:00 Gemini	11:00 Scorpio

MARCH 2

A.M.	P.M.
12:01 Scorpio	12:01 Gemini
1:00 Sagittarius	1:00 Cancer
2:00 Sagittarius	2:00 Cancer
3:00 Capricorn	3:00 Leo
4:00 Capricorn	4:00 Leo
5:00 Aquarius	5:00 Virgo
6:00 Aquarius	6:00 Virgo
7:00 Pisces	7:00 Virgo
8:00 Aries	8:00 Libra
9:00 Taurus	9:00 Libra
10:00 Taurus	10:00 Scorpio
11:00 Gemini	11:00 Scorpio

MARCH 17

A.M.	P.M.
12:01 Sagittarius	12:01 Gemini
1:00 Sagittarius	1:00 Cancer
2:00 Capricorn	2:00 Leo
3:00 Capricorn	3:00 Leo
4:00 Aquarius	4:00 Virgo
5:00 Aquarius	5:00 Virgo
6:00 Pisces	6:00 Virgo
7:00 Aries	7:00 Libra
8:00 Taurus	8:00 Libra
9:00 Taurus	9:00 Scorpio
10:00 Gemini	10:00 Scorpio
11:00 Gemini	11:00 Scorpio

MARCH 22

A.M.	P.M.
12:01 Sagittarius	12:01 Cancer
1:00 Sagittarius	1:00 Cancer
2:00 Capricorn	2:00 Leo
3:00 Capricorn	3:00 Leo
4:00 Aquarius	4:00 Virgo
5:00 Pisces	5:00 Virgo
6:00 Pisces	6:00 Virgo
7:00 Aries	7:00 Libra
8:00 Taurus	8:00 Libra
9:00 Gemini	9:00 Scorpio
10:00 Gemini	10:00 Scorpio
11:00 Cancer	11:00 Scorpio

APRIL 6

A.M.	P.M.
12:01 Sagittarius	12:01 Cancer
1:00 Capricorn	1:00 Leo
2:00 Capricorn	2:00 Leo
3:00 Aquarius	3:00 Virgo
4:00 Pisces	4:00 Virgo
5:00 Pisces	5:00 Virgo
6:00 Aries	6:00 Libra
7:00 Taurus	7:00 Libra
8:00 Gemini	8:00 Scorpio
9:00 Gemini	9:00 Scorpio
10:00 Cancer	10:00 Sagittarius
11:00 Cancer	11:00 Sagittarius

MARCH 27

A.M.	P.M.
12:01 Sagittarius	12:01 Cancer
1:00 Sagittarius	1:00 Leo
2:00 Capricorn	2:00 Leo
3:00 Capricorn	3:00 Leo
4:00 Aquarius	4:00 Virgo
5:00 Pisces	5:00 Virgo
6:00 Aries	6:00 Libra
7:00 Aries	7:00 Libra
8:00 Taurus	8:00 Libra
9:00 Gemini	9:00 Scorpio
10:00 Gemini	10:00 Scorpio
11:00 Cancer	11:00 Sagittarius

APRIL 11

A.M.	P.M.
12:01 Sagittarius	12:01 Leo
1:00 Capricorn	1:00 Leo
2:00 Capricorn	2:00 Leo
3:00 Aquarius	3:00 Virgo
4:00 Pisces	4:00 Virgo
5:00 Aries	5:00 Libra
6:00 Aries	6:00 Libra
7:00 Taurus	7:00 Libra
8:00 Gemini	8:00 Scorpio
9:00 Gemini	9:00 Scorpio
10:00 Cancer	10:00 Sagittarius
11:00 Cancer	11:00 Sagittarius

APRIL 1

A.M.	P.M.
12:01 Sagittarius	12:01 Cancer
1:00 Capricorn	1:00 Leo
2:00 Capricorn	2:00 Leo
3:00 Aquarius	3:00 Virgo
4:00 Aquarius	4:00 Virgo
5:00 Pisces	5:00 Virgo
6:00 Aries	6:00 Libra
7:00 Taurus	7:00 Libra
8:00 Taurus	8:00 Scorpio
9:00 Gemini	9:00 Scorpio
10:00 Gemini	10:00 Scorpio
11:00 Cancer	11:00 Sagittarius

APRIL 16

A.M.	P.M.
12:01 Capricorn	12:01 Leo
1:00 Capricorn	1:00 Leo
2:00 Aquarius	2:00 Virgo
3:00 Aquarius	3:00 Virgo
4:00 Pisces	4:00 Virgo
5:00 Aries	5:00 Libra
6:00 Taurus	6:00 Libra
7:00 Taurus	7:00 Scorpio
8:00 Gemini	8:00 Scorpio
9:00 Gemini	9:00 Scorpio
10:00 Cancer	10:00 Sagittarius
11:00 Cancer	11:00 Sagittarius

APRIL 21

A.M.	P.M.		
12:01 Capricorn	12:01 Leo		
1:00 Capricorn	1:00 Leo		
2:00 Aquarius	2:00 Virgo		
3:00 Pisces	3:00 Virgo		
4:00 Pisces	4:00 Virgo		
5:00 Aries	5:00 Libra		
6:00 Taurus	6:00 Libra		
7:00 Gemini	7:00 Scorpio		
8:00 Gemini	8:00 Scorpio		
9:00 Cancer	9:00 Scorpio		
10:00 Cancer	10:00 Sagittarius		
11:00 Cancer	11:00 Sagittarius		

MAY 6

A.M.	P.M.
12:01 Capricorn	12:01 Leo
1:00 Aquarius	1:00 Virgo
2:00 Pisces	2:00 Virgo
3:00 Pisces	3:00 Virgo
4:00 Aries	4:00 Libra
5:00 Taurus	5:00 Libra
6:00 Gemini	6:00 Scorpio
7:00 Gemini	7:00 Scorpio
8:00 Cancer	8:00 Scorpio
9:00 Cancer	9:00 Sagittarius
10:00 Cancer	10:00 Sagittarius
11:00 Leo	11:00 Capricorn

APRIL 26

A.M.	P.M.
12:01 Capricorn	12:01 Leo
1:00 Capricorn	1:00 Leo
2:00 Aquarius	2:00 Virgo
3:00 Pisces	3:00 Virgo
4:00 Aries	4:00 Libra
5:00 Aries	5:00 Libra
6:00 Taurus	6:00 Libra
7:00 Gemini	7:00 Scorpio
8:00 Gemini	8:00 Scorpio
9:00 Cancer	9:00 Sagittarius
10:00 Cancer	10:00 Sagittarius
11:00 Leo	11:00 Sagittarius

MAY 11

A.M.	P.M.
12:01 Capricorn	12:01 Leo
1:00 Aquarius	1:00 Virgo
2:00 Pisces	2:00 Virgo
3:00 Aries	3:00 Libra
4:00 Aries	4:00 Libra
5:00 Taurus	5:00 Libra
6:00 Gemini	6:00 Scorpio
7:00 Gemini	7:00 Scorpio
8:00 Cancer	8:00 Sagittarius
9:00 Cancer	9:00 Sagittarius
10:00 Leo	10:00 Sagittarius
11:00 Leo	11:00 Capricorn

MAY 1

A.M.	P.M.
12:01 Capricorn	12:01 Leo
1:00 Aquarius	1:00 Virgo
2:00 Aquarius	2:00 Virgo
3:00 Pisces	3:00 Virgo
4:00 Aries	4:00 Libra
5:00 Taurus	5:00 Libra
6:00 Taurus	6:00 Scorpio
7:00 Gemini	7:00 Scorpio
8:00 Gemini	8:00 Scorpio
9:00 Cancer	9:00 Sagittarius
10:00 Cancer	10:00 Sagittarius
11:00 Leo	11:00 Capricorn

MAY 16

A.M.	P.M.
12:01 Aquarius	12:01 Virgo
1:00 Aquarius	1:00 Virgo
2:00 Pisces	2:00 Virgo
3:00 Aries	3:00 Libra
4:00 Taurus	4:00 Libra
5:00 Taurus	5:00 Scorpio
6:00 Gemini	6:00 Scorpio
7:00 Gemini	7:00 Scorpio
8:00 Cancer	8:00 Sagittarius
9:00 Cancer	9:00 Sagittarius
10:00 Leo	10:00 Capricorn
11:00 Leo	11:00 Capricorn

MAY 21

A.M.	P.M.
12:01 Aquarius	12:01 Virgo
1:00 Pisces	1:00 Virgo
2:00 Pisces	2:00 Virgo
3:00 Aries	3:00 Libra
4:00 Taurus	4:00 Libra
5:00 Gemini	5:00 Scorpio
6:00 Gemini	6:00 Scorpio
7:00 Cancer	7:00 Scorpio
8:00 Cancer	8:00 Sagittarius
9:00 Cancer	9:00 Sagittarius
10:00 Leo	10:00 Capricorn
11:00 Leo	11:00 Capricorn

JUNE 5

A.M.	P.M.
12:01 Pisces	12:01 Virgo
1:00 Pisces	1:00 Virgo
2:00 Aries	2:00 Libra
3:00 Taurus	3:00 Libra
4:00 Gemini	4:00 Scorpio
5:00 Gemini	5:00 Scorpio
6:00 Cancer	6:00 Scorpio
7:00 Cancer	7:00 Sagittarius
8:00 Cancer	8:00 Sagittarius
9:00 Leo	9:00 Capricorn
10:00 Leo	10:00 Capricorn
11:00 Virgo	11:00 Aquarius

MAY 26

A.M.	P.M.
12:01 Aquarius	12:01 Virgo
1:00 Pisces	1:00 Virgo
2:00 Aries	2:00 Libra
3:00 Aries	3:00 Libra
4:00 Taurus	4:00 Libra
5:00 Gemini	5:00 Scorpio
6:00 Gemini	6:00 Scorpio
7:00 Cancer	7:00 Sagittarius
8:00 Cancer	8:00 Sagittarius
9:00 Leo	9:00 Sagittarius
10:00 Leo	10:00 Capricorn
11:00 Leo	11:00 Capricorn

JUNE 10

A.M.	P.M.
12:01 Pisces	12:01 Virgo
1:00 Aries	1:00 Libra
2:00 Aries	2:00 Libra
3:00 Taurus	3:00 Libra
4:00 Gemini	4:00 Scorpio
5:00 Gemini	5:00 Scorpio
6:00 Cancer	6:00 Sagittarius
7:00 Cancer	7:00 Sagittarius
8:00 Leo	8:00 Sagittarius
9:00 Leo	9:00 Capricorn
10:00 Leo	10:00 Capricorn
11:00 Virgo	11:00 Aquarius

MAY 31

A.M.	P.M.
12:01 Aquarius	12:01 Virgo
1:00 Pisces	1:00 Virgo
2:00 Aries	2:00 Libra
3:00 Taurus	3:00 Libra
4:00 Taurus	4:00 Scorpio
5:00 Gemini	5:00 Scorpio
6:00 Gemini	6:00 Scorpio
7:00 Cancer	7:00 Sagittarius
8:00 Cancer	8:00 Sagittarius
9:00 Leo	9:00 Capricorn
10:00 Leo	10:00 Capricorn
11:00 Virgo	11:00 Aquarius

JUNE 15

A.M.	P.M.
12:01 Pisces	12:01 Virgo
1:00 Aries	1:00 Libra
2:00 Taurus	2:00 Libra
3:00 Taurus	3:00 Scorpio
4:00 Gemini	4:00 Scorpio
5:00 Gemini	5:00 Scorpio
6:00 Cancer	6:00 Sagittarius
7:00 Cancer	7:00 Sagittarius
8:00 Leo	8:00 Capricorn
9:00 Leo	9:00 Capricorn
10:00 Virgo	10:00 Aquarius
11:00 Virgo	11:00 Aquarius

JUNE 20

A.M.	P.M.
12:01 Pisces	12:01 Virgo
1:00 Aries	1:00 Libra
2:00 Taurus	2:00 Libra
3:00 Gemini	3:00 Scorpio
4:00 Gemini	4:00 Scorpio
5:00 Cancer	5:00 Scorpio
6:00 Cancer	6:00 Sagittarius
7:00 Cancer	7:00 Sagittarius
8:00 Leo	8:00 Capricorn
9:00 Leo	9:00 Capricorn
10:00 Virgo	10:00 Aquarius
11:00 Virgo	11:00 Pisces

JULY 10

A.M.	P.M.
12:01 Aries	12:01 Libra
1:00 Taurus	1:00 Libra
2:00 Gemini	2:00 Scorpio
3:00 Gemini	3:00 Scorpio
4:00 Cancer	4:00 Sagittarius
5:00 Cancer	5:00 Sagittarius
6:00 Leo	6:00 Sagittarius
7:00 Leo	7:00 Capricorn
8:00 Leo	8:00 Capricorn
9:00 Virgo	9:00 Aquarius
10:00 Virgo	10:00 Pisces
11:00 Libra	11:00 Aries

JUNE 30

A.M.	P.M.
12:01 Aries	12:01 Libra
1:00 Taurus	1:00 Libra
2:00 Taurus	2:00 Scorpio
3:00 Gemini	3:00 Scorpio
4:00 Gemini	4:00 Scorpio
5:00 Cancer	5:00 Sagittarius
6:00 Cancer	6:00 Sagittarius
7:00 Leo	7:00 Capricorn
8:00 Leo	8:00 Capricorn
9:00 Virgo	9:00 Aquarius
10:00 Virgo	10:00 Aquarius
11:00 Virgo	11:00 Pisces

JULY 15

A.M.	P.M.
12:01 Taurus	12:01 Libra
1:00 Taurus	1:00 Libra
2:00 Gemini	2:00 Scorpio
3:00 Gemini	3:00 Scorpio
4:00 Cancer	4:00 Sagittarius
5:00 Cancer	5:00 Sagittarius
6:00 Leo	6:00 Capricorn
7:00 Leo	7:00 Capricorn
8:00 Leo	8:00 Aquarius
9:00 Virgo	9:00 Aquarius
10:00 Virgo	10:00 Pisces
11:00 Libra	11:00 Aries

JULY 5

A.M.	P.M.
12:01 Aries	12:01 Libra
1:00 Taurus	1:00 Libra
2:00 Gemini	2:00 Scorpio
3:00 Gemini	3:00 Scorpio
4:00 Cancer	4:00 Scorpio
5:00 Cancer	5:00 Sagittarius
6:00 Cancer	6:00 Sagittarius
7:00 Leo	7:00 Capricorn
8:00 Leo	8:00 Capricorn
9:00 Virgo	9:00 Capricorn
10:00 Virgo	10:00 Pisces
11:00 Virgo	11:00 Pisces

JULY 20

A.M.	P.M.
12:01 Taurus	12:01 Libra
1:00 Gemini	1:00 Scorpio
2:00 Gemini	2:00 Scorpio
3:00 Cancer	3:00 Scorpio
4:00 Cancer	4:00 Sagittarius
5:00 Cancer	5:00 Sagittarius
6:00 Leo	6:00 Capricorn
7:00 Leo	7:00 Capricorn
8:00 Virgo	8:00 Aquarius
9:00 Virgo	9:00 Pisces
10:00 Virgo	10:00 Pisces
11:00 Libra	11:00 Aries

JULY 25

A.M.	P.M.
12:01 Taurus	12:01 Libra
1:00 Gemini	1:00 Scorpio
2:00 Gemini	2:00 Scorpio
3:00 Cancer	3:00 Sagittarius
4:00 Cancer	4:00 Sagittarius
5:00 Leo	5:00 Sagittarius
6:00 Leo	6:00 Capricorn
7:00 Leo	7:00 Capricorn
8:00 Virgo	8:00 Aquarius
9:00 Virgo	9:00 Pisces
10:00 Libra	10:00 Aries
11:00 Libra	11:00 Aries

AUGUST 9

A.M.	P.M.
12:01 Gemini	12:01 Scorpio
1:00 Gemini	1:00 Scorpio
2:00 Cancer	2:00 Sagittarius
3:00 Cancer	3:00 Sagittarius
4:00 Leo	4:00 Sagittarius
5:00 Leo	5:00 Capricorn
6:00 Leo	6:00 Capricorn
7:00 Virgo	7:00 Aquarius
8:00 Virgo	8:00 Pisces
9:00 Libra	9:00 Aries
10:00 Libra	10:00 Aries
11:00 Libra	11:00 Aries

JULY 30

A.M.	P.M.
12:01 Taurus	12:01 Libra
1:00 Gemini	1:00 Scorpio
2:00 Gemini	2:00 Scorpio
3:00 Cancer	3:00 Sagittarius
4:00 Cancer	4:00 Sagittarius
5:00 Leo	5:00 Capricorn
6:00 Leo	6:00 Capricorn
7:00 Leo	7:00 Aquarius
8:00 Virgo	8:00 Aquarius
9:00 Virgo	9:00 Pisces
10:00 Libra	10:00 Aries
11:00 Libra	11:00 Taurus

AUGUST 14

A.M.	P.M.
12:01 Gemini	12:01 Scorpio
1:00 Gemini	1:00 Scorpio
2:00 Cancer	2:00 Sagittarius
3:00 Cancer	3:00 Sagittarius
4:00 Leo	4:00 Capricorn
5:00 Leo	5:00 Capricorn
6:00 Leo	6:00 Aquarius
7:00 Virgo	7:00 Aquarius
8:00 Virgo	8:00 Pisces
9:00 Libra	9:00 Aries
10:00 Libra	10:00 Taurus
11:00 Libra	11:00 Taurus

AUGUST 4

A.M.	P.M.
12:01 Gemini	12:01 Scorpio
1:00 Gemini	1:00 Scorpio
2:00 Cancer	2:00 Scorpio
3:00 Cancer	3:00 Sagittarius
4:00 Cancer	4:00 Sagittarius
5:00 Leo	5:00 Capricorn
6:00 Leo	6:00 Capricorn
7:00 Virgo	7:00 Aquarius
8:00 Virgo	8:00 Aquarius
9:00 Virgo	9:00 Pisces
10:00 Libra	10:00 Aries
11:00 Libra	11:00 Taurus

AUGUST 19

A.M.	P.M.
12:01 Gemini	12:01 Scorpio
1:00 Cancer	1:00 Scorpio
2:00 Cancer	2:00 Sagittarius
3:00 Cancer	3:00 Sagittarius
4:00 Leo	4:00 Capricorn
5:00 Leo	5:00 Capricorn
6:00 Virgo	6:00 Aquarius
7:00 Virgo	7:00 Pisces
8:00 Virgo	8:00 Pisces
9:00 Libra	9:00 Aries
10:00 Libra	10:00 Taurus
11:00 Scorpio	11:00 Gemini

AUGUST 24

A.M.	P.M.
12:01 Gemini	12:01 Scorpio
1:00 Cancer	1:00 Sagittarius
2:00 Cancer	2:00 Sagittarius
3:00 Leo	3.00 Sagittarius
4:00 Leo	4:00 Capricorn
5:00 Leo	5:00 Capricorn
6:00 Virgo	6:00 Aquarius
7:00 Virgo	7:00 Pisces
8:00 Libra	8:00 Aries
9:00 Libra	9:00 Aries
10:00 Libra	10:00 Taurus
11:00 Scorpio	11:00 Gemini

SEPTEMBER 8

A.M.	P.M.
12:01 Cancer	12:01 Sagittarius
1:00 Cancer	1:00 Sagittarius
2:00 Leo	2:00 Sagittarius
3:00 Leo	3:00 Capricorn
4:00 Leo	4:00 Capricorn
5:00 Virgo	5:00 Aquarius
6:00 Virgo	6:00 Pisces
7:00 Libra	7:00 Aries
8:00 Libra	8:00 Aries
9:00 Libra	9:00 Taurus
10:00 Scorpio	10:00 Gemini
11:00 Scorpio	11:00 Gemini

AUGUST 29

A.M.	P.M.
12:01 Gemini	12:01 Scorpio
1:00 Cancer	1:00 Sagittarius
2:00 Cancer	2:00 Sagittarius
3:00 Leo	3:00 Capricorn
4:00 Leo	4:00 Capricorn
5:00 Leo	5:00 Aquarius
6:00 Virgo	6:00 Aquarius
7:00 Virgo	7:00 Pisces
8:00 Libra	8:00 Aries
9:00 Libra	9:00 Taurus
10:00 Libra	10:00 Taurus
11:00 Scorpio	11:00 Gemini

SEPTEMBER 13

A.M.	P.M.
12:01 Cancer	12:01 Sagittarius
1:00 Cancer	1:00 Sagittarius
2:00 Leo	2:00 Capricorn
3:00 Leo	3:00 Capricorn
4:00 Leo	4:00 Aquarius
5:00 Virgo	5:00 Aquarius
6:00 Virgo	6:00 Pisces
7:00 Libra	7:00 Aries
8:00 Libra	8:00 Taurus
9:00 Scorpio	9:00 Taurus
10:00 Scorpio	10:00 Gemini
11:00 Scorpio	11:00 Gemini

SEPTEMBER 3

A.M.	P.M.
12:01 Cancer	12:01 Scorpio
1:00 Cancer	1:00 Sagittarius
2:00 Cancer	2:00 Sagittarius
3:00 Leo	3:00 Capricorn
4:00 Leo	4:00 Capricorn
5:00 Virgo	5:00 Aquarius
6:00 Virgo	6:00 Aquarius
7:00 Virgo	7:00 Pisces
8:00 Libra	8:00 Aries
9:00 Libra	9:00 Taurus
10:00 Scorpio	10:00 Gemini
11:00 Scorpio	11:00 Gemini

SEPTEMBER 18

A.M.	P.M.
12:01 Cancer	12:01 Sagittarius
1:00 Cancer	1:00 Sagittarius
2:00 Leo	2:00 Capricorn
3:00 Leo	3:00 Capricorn
4:00 Virgo	4:00 Aquarius
5:00 Virgo	5:00 Aquarius
6:00 Virgo	6:00 Pisces
7:00 Libra	7:00 Aries
8:00 Libra	8:00 Taurus
9:00 Scorpio	9:00 Gemini
10:00 Scorpio	10:00 Gemini
11:00 Scorpio	11:00 Cancer

SEPTEMBER 23

A.M.	P.M.
12:01 Cancer	12:01 Sagittarius
1:00 Leo	1:00 Sagittarius
2:00 Leo	2:00 Capricorn
3:00 Leo	3:00 Capricorn
4:00 Virgo	4:00 Aquarius
5:00 Virgo	5:00 Pisces
6:00 Libra	6:00 Aries
7:00 Libra	7:00 Aries
8:00 Libra	8:00 Taurus
9:00 Scorpio	9:00 Gemini
10:00 Scorpio	10:00 Gemini
11:00 Sagittarius	11:00 Cancer

OCTOBER 8

A.M.	P.M.
12:01 Leo	12:01 Sagittarius
1:00 Leo	1:00 Capricorn
2:00 Leo	2:00 Capricorn
3:00 Virgo	3:00 Aquarius
4:00 Virgo	4:00 Pisces
5:00 Libra	5:00 Aries
6:00 Libra	6:00 Aries
7:00 Libra	7:00 Taurus
8:00 Scorpio	8:00 Gemini
9:00 Scorpio	9:00 Gemini
10:00 Sagittarius	10:00 Cancer
11:00 Sagittarius	11:00 Cancer

SEPTEMBER 28

A.M.	P.M.
12:01 Cancer	12:01 Sagittarius
1:00 Leo	1:00 Capricorn
2:00 Leo	2:00 Capricorn
3:00 Leo	3:00 Aquarius
4:00 Virgo	4:00 Aquarius
5:00 Virgo	5:00 Pisces
6:00 Libra	6:00 Aries
7:00 Libra	7:00 Taurus
8:00 Libra	8:00 Taurus
9:00 Scorpio	9:00 Gemini
10:00 Scorpio	10:00 Gemini
11:00 Sagittarius	11:00 Cancer

OCTOBER 13

A.M.	P.M.
12:01 Leo	12:01 Capricorn
1:00 Leo	1:00 Capricorn
2:00 Leo	2:00 Aquarius
3:00 Virgo	3:00 Aquarius
4:00 Virgo	4:00 Pisces
5:00 Libra	5:00 Aries
6:00 Libra	6:00 Taurus
7:00 Libra	7:00 Taurus
8:00 Scorpio	8:00 Gemini
9:00 Scorpio	9:00 Gemini
10:00 Sagittarius	10:00 Cancer
11:00 Sagittarius	11:00 Cancer

OCTOBER 3

A.M.	P.M.
12:01 Cancer	12:01 Sagittarius
1:00 Leo	1:00 Capricorn
2:00 Leo	2:00 Capricorn
3:00 Virgo	3:00 Aquarius
4:00 Virgo	4:00 Pisces
5:00 Virgo	5:00 Pisces
6:00 Libra	6:00 Aries
7:00 Libra	7:00 Taurus
8:00 Scorpio	8:00 Gemini
9:00 Scorpio	9:00 Gemini
10:00 Scorpio	10:00 Cancer
11:00 Sagittarius	11:00 Cancer

OCTOBER 18

A.M.	P.M.
12:01 Leo	12:01 Capricorn
1:00 Leo	1:00 Capricorn
2:00 Virgo	2:00 Aquarius
3:00 Virgo	3:00 Pisces
4:00 Virgo	4:00 Pisces
5:00 Libra	5:00 Aries
6:00 Libra	6:00 Taurus
7:00 Scorpio	7:00 Taurus
8:00 Scorpio	8:00 Gemini
9:00 Scorpio	9:00 Gemini
10:00 Sagittarius	10:00 Cancer
11:00 Sagittarius	11:00 Cancer

OCTOBER 23

A.M.	P.M.
12:01 Leo	12:01 Capricorn
1:00 Leo	1:00 Capricorn
2:00 Virgo	2:00 Aquarius
3:00 Virgo	3:00 Pisces
4:00 Virgo	4:00 Aries
5:00 Libra	5:00 Aries
6:00 Libra	6:00 Taurus
7:00 Scorpio	7:00 Gemini
8:00 Scorpio	8:00 Gemini
9:00 Sagittarius	9:00 Cancer
10:00 Sagittarius	10:00 Cancer
11:00 Sagittarius	11:00 Leo

NOVEMBER 7

A.M.	P.M.
12:01 Leo	12:01 Capricorn
1:00 Virgo	1:00 Aquarius
2:00 Virgo	2:00 Pisces
3:00 Libra	3:00 Aries
4:00 Libra	4:00 Aries
5:00 Libra	5:00 Taurus
6:00 Scorpio	6:00 Gemini
7:00 Scorpio	7:00 Gemini
8:00 Sagittarius	8:00 Cancer
9:00 Sagittarius	9:00 Cancer
10:00 Sagittarius	10:00 Leo
11:00 Capricorn	11:00 Leo

OCTOBER 28

A.M.	P.M.
12:01 Leo	12:01 Capricorn
1:00 Leo	1:00 Aquarius
2:00 Virgo	2:00 Aquarius
3:00 Virgo	3:00 Pisces
4:00 Libra	4:00 Aries
5:00 Libra	5:00 Taurus
6:00 Libra	6:00 Taurus
7:00 Scorpio	7:00 Gemini
8:00 Scorpio	8:00 Gemini
9:00 Sagittarius	9:00 Cancer
10:00 Sagittarius	10:00 Cancer
11:00 Capricorn	11:00 Leo

NOVEMBER 12

A.M.	P.M.
12:01 Leo	12:01 Aquarius
1:00 Virgo	1:00 Aquarius
2:00 Virgo	2:00 Pisces
3:00 Libra	3:00 Aries
4:00 Libra	4:00 Taurus
5:00 Libra	5:00 Taurus
6:00 Scorpio	6:00 Gemini
7:00 Scorpio	7:00 Gemini
8:00 Sagittarius	8:00 Cancer
9:00 Sagittarius	9:00 Cancer
10:00 Capricorn	10:00 Leo
11:00 Capricorn	11:00 Leo

NOVEMBER 2

A.M.	P.M.
12:01 Leo	12:01 Capricorn
1:00 Virgo	1:00 Aquarius
2:00 Virgo	2:00 Aquarius
3:00 Virgo	3:00 Pisces
4:00 Libra	4:00 Aries
5:00 Libra	5:00 Taurus
6:00 Scorpio	6:00 Taurus
7:00 Scorpio	7:00 Gemini
8:00 Scorpio	8:00 Gemini
9:00 Sagittarius	9:00 Cancer
10:00 Sagittarius	10:00 Cancer
11:00 Capricorn	11:00 Leo

NOVEMBER 17

A.M.	P.M.
12:01 Virgo	12:01 Aquarius
1:00 Virgo	1:00 Aquarius
2:00 Virgo	2:00 Pisces
3:00 Libra	3:00 Aries
4:00 Libra	4:00 Taurus
5:00 Scorpio	5:00 Taurus
6:00 Scorpio	6:00 Gemini
7:00 Scorpio	7:00 Gemini
8:00 Sagittarius	8:00 Cancer
9:00 Sagittarius	9:00 Cancer
10:00 Capricorn	10:00 Leo
11:00 Capricorn	11:00 Leo

NOVEMBER 22

A.M.	P.M.
12:01 Virgo	12:01 Aquarius
1:00 Virgo	1:00 Pisces
2:00 Libra	2:00 Pisces
3:00 Libra	3:00 Aries
4:00 Libra	4:00 Taurus
5:00 Scorpio	5:00 Gemini
6:00 Scorpio	6:00 Gemini
7:00 Scorpio	7:00 Cancer
8:00 Sagittarius	8:00 Cancer
9:00 Sagittarius	9:00 Cancer
10:00 Capricorn	10:00 Leo
11:00 Capricorn	11:00 Leo

DECEMBER 7

A.M.	P.M.
12:01 Virgo	12:01 Pisces
1:00 Virgo	1:00 Aries
2:00 Libra	2:00 Aries
3:00 Libra	3:00 Taurus
4:00 Scorpio	4:00 Gemini
5:00 Scorpio	5:00 Gemini
6:00 Sagittarius	6:00 Cancer
7:00 Sagittarius	7:00 Cancer
8:00 Sagittarius	8:00 Cancer
9:00 Capricorn	9:00 Leo
10:00 Capricorn	10:00 Leo
11:00 Aquarius	11:00 Virgo

NOVEMBER 27

A.M.	P.M.
12:01 Virgo	12:01 Aquarius
1:00 Virgo	1:00 Pisces
2:00 Libra	2:00 Aries
3:00 Libra	3:00 Taurus
4:00 Libra	4:00 Taurus
5:00 Scorpio	5:00 Gemini
6:00 Scorpio	6:00 Gemini
7:00 Sagittarius	7:00 Cancer
8:00 Sagittarius	8:00 Cancer
9:00 Capricorn	9:00 Leo
10:00 Capricorn	10:00 Leo
11:00 Aquarius	11:00 Leo

DECEMBER 12

A.M.	P.M.
12:01 Virgo	12:01 Pisces
1:00 Libra	1:00 Aries
2:00 Libra	2:00 Taurus
3:00 Libra	3:00 Taurus
4:00 Scorpio	4:00 Gemini
5:00 Scorpio	5:00 Gemini
6:00 Sagittarius	6:00 Cancer
7:00 Sagittarius	7:00 Cancer
8:00 Capricorn	8:00 Leo
9:00 Capricorn	9:00 Leo
10:00 Aquarius	10:00 Leo
11:00 Aquarius	11:00 Virgo

DECEMBER 2

A.M.	P.M.
12:01 Virgo	12:01 Aquarius
1:00 Virgo	1:00 Pisces
2:00 Libra	2:00 Aries
3:00 Libra	3:00 Taurus
4:00 Scorpio	4:00 Taurus
5:00 Scorpio	5:00 Gemini
6:00 Scorpio	6:00 Gemini
7:00 Sagittarius	7:00 Cancer
8:00 Sagittarius	8:00 Cancer
9:00 Capricorn	9:00 Leo
10:00 Capricorn	10:00 Leo
11:00 Aquarius	11:00 Virgo

DECEMBER 17

A.M.	P.M.
12:01 Virgo	12:01 Pisces
1:00 Libra	1:00 Aries
2:00 Libra	2:00 Taurus
3:00 Scorpio	3:00 Taurus
4:00 Scorpio	4:00 Gemini
5:00 Scorpio	5:00 Gemini
6:00 Sagittarius	6:00 Cancer
7:00 Sagittarius	7:00 Cancer
8:00 Capricorn	8:00 Leo
9:00 Capricorn	9:00 Leo
10:00 Aquarius	10:00 Virgo
11:00 Aquarius	11:00 Virgo

DECEMBER 22

A.M.	P.M.
12:01 Virgo	12:01 Aries
1:00 Libra	1:00 Aries
2:00 Libra	2:00 Taurus
3:00 Scorpio	3:00 Gemini
4:00 Scorpio	4:00 Gemini
5:00 Sagittarius	5:00 Cancer
6:00 Sagittarius	6:00 Cancer
7:00 Sagittarius	7:00 Cancer
8:00 Capricorn	8:00 Leo
9:00 Capricorn	9:00 Leo
10:00 Aquarius	10:00 Virgo
11:00 Pisces	11:00 Virgo

DECEMBER 27

A.M.	P.M.
12:01 Libra	12:01 Aries
1:00 Libra	1:00 Taurus
2:00 Libra	2:00 Taurus
3:00 Scorpio	3:00 Gemini
4:00 Scorpio	4:00 Gemini
5:00 Sagittarius	5:00 Cancer
6:00 Sagittarius	6:00 Cancer
7:00 Capricorn	7:00 Leo
8:00 Capricorn	8:00 Leo
9:00 Aquarius	9:00 Leo
10:00 Aquarius	10:00 Virgo
11:00 Pisces	11:00 Virgo

APPENDIX VI   Indian Medical Astrology
By M. K. Gandhi

Grateful acknowledgment is made to Pundit Chakkradhar Joshi, author of the Hindu text, *Giadavali,* for assistance in the preparation of these notes on the Indian system of medical astrology.

Before applying the following rules for astrological diagnosis, the horoscope has to be converted into the *Nirayana System* by deducting $22° - 9' - 19''$ in horoscopes of April 15, 1878, and then onward each month $4'' - 2$ more deductions. Thus, on May 15, 1878, it should be

$$22° - 9' - 19''$$
$$+ \quad 4.2$$
$$\overline{22° - 9' - 23''.2}$$

DISEASES OF THE HEAD

(A) Moon's north node; Mars and Saturn in one House.
(B) When the Ascendant is Aries, Scorpio, Capricorn or Aquarius, and Moon and Jupiter together with Mars, Saturn, Uranus, and Pluto.

DISEASE OF THE EYES

(A) Lord of the signs of the Second and Twelfth Houses placed in Third House.

(B) Lord of Second House with Saturn and Mars.
(C) Mars, Saturn, Uranus, or Pluto in Second House and when Saturn is in Fifth, Eighth, or Twelfth House.
(D) There is trouble with *left eye* when Lord of First or Eighth House is in Sixth House.
(E) There is trouble with *right eye* when Venus is in Sixth House.
(F) When Saturn, Mars, Moon, and Sun are in Second, Sixth, Eighth, or Twelfth House.

DISEASES OF THE TONGUE

Ruler of the Second Houses together with Mercury or Jupiter.

DISEASES OF THE FACE AND MOUTH

(A) Ruler of Ascendant in Aries or Scorpio or Gemini or Virgo and Mercury in Seventh House.
(B) Ruler of the First House together with Mercury placed in Aries or Scorpio.
(C) Mars and Sun together in Second House.
(D) Jupiter or Venus is ruler of Sixth House and placed in First House and Mars; Saturn, Uranus, or Pluto in Seventh House.

DENTAL DISEASES

(A) Ascendant Aries, Taurus, or Sagittarius and when Saturn is in Fourth, Seventh, or Eleventh House or Mars in Eighth, or Tenth House or Uranus and Pluto in Seventh House.
(B) Jupiter and Moon's North node (Rahu) in First House.
(C) Venus and Saturn in Eighth House, Mars, Saturn,

Uranus, Pluto, and Moon's nodes in Sixth House, Ruler of the Sixth House in Seventh House.
(D) Ruler of the Sixth House in Aries or in Scorpio. Ruler of the First House with Mars and Saturn in Fourth, Seventh, and Eleventh House.
(E) If Ruler of the Second House is with Ruler of the Sixth House.
(F) Moon's North or South node in Sixth House. This planetary position also brings diseases of *lips*.
(G) Moon's North node in First or Fifth House.
(H) Mars, Saturn, Uranus, or Moon's nodes in Seventh House and Sun Moon in Seventh House cause the full teeth to appear at a much earlier than normal age.

DISEASES OF THE PALATE

Ruler of the Second House and Mercury in Sixth House, and Moon's North or South node with them.

DISEASES OF THE NOSE

Moon in Sixth House, Saturn in Eighth House, and Mars, Saturn, Uranus, Pluto, or Moon's node.

DISEASES OF THE EARS

(A) Ruler of the Second House in First House with Mars.
(B) Mars or Venus in Second or Twelfth House.
(C) Mars, Saturn, Uranus, Pluto, or Moon's node in Third House or Mars in Eighth, Ninth, or Twelfth, Saturn in First, Sixth, and Ninth House, Uranus or Pluto or Moon's nodes in Ninth House.
(D) Ruler of the Eleventh House with Mars or Saturn or Uranus or Pluto or Moon's node or one or more of

these planets seventh from the position of the Ruler of the Eleventh House. If Saturn is in Fourth or Eleventh House or Mars in Sixth or Tenth House House from the position of the Ruler of Eleventh House, there will be ear trouble.

DISEASES OF THE THROAT

Ruler of the Third House with Mercury.

DISEASES OF THE CHEST OR HEART

(A) Mars, Saturn, Uranus, Pluto, or Moon's node (one or more than one of these) in Fourth House.
(B) Ruler of the Fourth with one or more of the planets mentioned in (A).
(C) Mars, Jupiter, Saturn in Fourth House.

DISEASES OF ABDOMINAL AND PELVIC REGIONS

(A) Saturn and Venus in Eighth House, Mars or Saturn, Uranus, Pluto or Moon's nodes (one or more than one) in Sixth House and Ruler of Sixth in Seventh House.
(B) Saturn in Eight House and Moon in First House.
(C) Moon's South or North node in Seventh House.
(D) Ruler of the Sixth in Seventh House with Mars or Saturn or Uranus or Pluto or Moon's nodes and in Sixth or Eighth House. Mars or Saturn or Uranus or Pluto or Moon's nodes (one or more than one of the planets).
(E) Moon and Venus in Sixth or Eighth House and Saturn Fourth or Seventh or Eleventh and Mars Eighth or Tenth House from Sixth or Eighth House

or Uranus or Pluto or Rahu in Seventh House from
Sixth or Eighth House.

(F) Jupiter in Sixth House and Moon in Sagittarius or
Pisces brings disease of pelvic region at the age of
19 or 22.

DISEASES OF THE URINARY SYSTEM, KIDNEY, OR BLADDER

(A) Mars in Seventh House with Saturn or Uranus, Pluto
or Moon's nodes (one or more than one of these)
or Saturn in Fourth or Eleventh House from Seventh
House or Uranus, Pluto Moon's nodes (one or more
than one) First House.

(B) Saturn in Seventh House with Moon's node in First
House.

DISEASES OF REPRODUCTIVE ORGANS OR EXCESSIVE, OBSESSIVE, OR COMPULSIVE SEXUAL BEHAVIOR

(A) Mars, Saturn, Uranus, Pluto, Moon's nodes (one or
more than one of these planets) in Eighth House or
in Second House. Also Saturn Fourth and Eleventh
from Eighth House or Mars Sixth or Tenth from
Eighth House and Moon in Twelfth House of the
Horoscope and Venus and Jupiter in Seventh or
Eighth House of the Horoscope.

(B) Moon, Saturn, Sun, and Mars in Second or Sixth,
or Eighth or Twelfth House.

DISEASES OF THE RECTUM: TUMORS, PILES, ULCER

(A) Ruler of the First House in Fourth or Twelfth House
with Mars, Mercury, or Ruler of First House and

Mercury in Twelfth House and Mars in Third, Eleventh, or Twelfth House.

(B) Ruler of the Sixth House in Eighth House with Mars, Saturn, Uranus, or Pluto, Moon's node (one or more than one).

(C) Ruler of the First House, Mercury, Mars in sign Leo in Fourth or Twelfth House.

(D) Ruler of the First House in Gemini or Virgo with Mercury or Mercury in Sagittarius or Pisces.

DISEASES OF THE GENITAL ORGANS

(A) Mars, Saturn, Uranus, Pluto, Moon's nodes (one or more than one) in Eighth House.

(B) Ruler of the Sixth House with Mercury and Mars.

(C) Ruler of the Sixth House with Mars, Moon, Jupiter, Venus in other than Seventh House on the position of the Ruler of the Sixth House.

(D) Mars with Ruler of the First House in Sixth House.

DISEASES OF THE SCROTUM

(A) Moon's North node with Saturn or Mars in First House.

(B) Ruler of the First House in Eighth House with Saturn or Moon's North node.

(C) Mars and Moon's North node or Saturn and Moon's North node together in conjunction in any House.

(D) Venus with Mars in Eighth House.

(E) Venus and Mars together in Aries or Scorpio.

(F) Venus and Moon together in Aries or Scorpio.

DISEASES OF THE AREA AROUND THE RECTUM

Ruler of the First House in Aries or Scorpio or Gemini or Virgo.

DISEASES OF THE FEET

Saturn or Saturn and Venus in Sixth House.

DISEASES OF CHEMICAL IMBALANCE

(A) Ruler of First House in Sixth, Eighth, or Twelfth House with Mercury.

(B) Sun in Sixth House with Mars, Saturn, Uranus, Pluto, Moon's node (with one or more than one).

(C) Mars, Saturn, Uranus, Pluto, Moon's nodes (one or more than one) in Second House, Mars in Cancer, Sun in Eighth House.

(D) When Venus is ruler of Sixth with Saturn in signs Aries, Leo, and Sagittarius.

(E) Venus when ruler of the Sixth House and Saturn Fourth or Tenth or Eleventh House from Venus.

(F) Mars in Sixth, Seventh, or Tenth House and Moon's North node in Second or Sixth or Eighth House.

DISEASES OF THE NERVES

(A) Jupiter in First House and Saturn in Seventh House.

(B) Saturn in First House and Mars in Fifth, Seventh, or Ninth House.

(C) Moon in Scorpio in Twelfth House with Saturn.

(D) Moon in First House with Mars or Saturn or Uranus

255

or Pluto or Moon's nodes (with one or more than one of the planets).

(E) If Saturn is in Sixth House and ruler of the First House is in First House, then sickness of the nerves comes at the age of 59.

MORE THAN ONE DISEASE

(A) Mars, Saturn, Uranus, Pluto, Moon's nodes in First, Fourth, Seventh, or Tenth House (one or more than one in one House).

(B) Moon in Sixth House with Mars, Saturn, Uranus, Pluto, Moon's nodes (with one or more than one).

(C) Saturn First, Fifth, Ninth, or Twelfth House with Mars, Uranus, Pluto, Moon's nodes (with one or more than one).

(D) Saturn and Mars in Sixth House.

(E) Ruler of the Sixth with ruler of First, Sixth, Eighth, or Twelfth House.

(F) Ruler of First House in First House with ruler of Sixth, Eighth, or Twelfth House.

(G) Mars, Saturn, Uranus, Pluto, Moon's nodes (one or more than one) in Fifth House and Ruler of First House in Eighth House with Mars or Saturn, or Uranus, or Pluto or Moon's nodes.

(H) Ruler of the Eighth in Sixth or Eighth or Twelfth House.

(I) More than three or four malefic planets such as Mars, Saturn, Uranus, Pluto, Moon's node in one House.

(J) Moon in Twelfth House, and in Seventh, Tenth, or Twelfth House, Mars, Saturn, Uranus, Pluto, or Moon's nodes in Seventh, Tenth, or Twelfth House.

(K) Mars and Saturn in Second House.

DISEASES OF THE BLOOD

(A) Saturn, Mars together in First, Sixth, Seventh, or Twelfth House and Sun in Seventh House from the position of Saturn and Mars.

(B) Ruler of the Second House with Mars or Mars in Sixth, Seventh, or Tenth House from the position of the Ruler of the Second House.
Mars in Second House and Sun in Eighth House.

CHRONIC ILLNESSES

Ruler of First House in its weak sign, Saturn and Mars in Sixth House, and Sun and Moon's node in Twelfth House.

DISEASES OF THE LYMPHATIC GLANDS

Sun and Venus in Seventh House, and Mars, Saturn, Uranus, Pluto Moon's nodes (one or more) in First House. Also Mars in Sixth, Tenth House from Seventh House and Saturn Fourth and Eleventh House from Seventh House.

RHEUMATISM

Ruler of First House and Jupiter in Sixth, Eighth, and Twelfth House.

FEVERS DUE TO INFECTION IN THE BLOOD

(A) Saturn with Moon's North node, Sun, and Mars.

(B) When Mars is in Sixth House, Ruler of the Sixth in Eighth House, at age of 6 or 12, illness of fever comes.

DISEASES OF URINARY ORGANS

(A) Saturn, Sun, and Venus in Fifth House.
(B) Mars in Seventh House and Sun in First House.
(C) Mars in Tenth House and Saturn in Fourth, Seventh, and Eleventh House from the position of Mars.
(D) Jupiter in Sixth House with Mars, Saturn, Uranus, Pluto, or Moon's nodes (one or more).

DISEASES OF NUTRITIONAL DEFICIENCY

(A) Ruler of the First House and Venus in Sixth, Eighth, or Twelfth House.
(B) Saturn in Fourth, Seventh, or First House and Mars in Sixth, Seventh, or Tenth House.
(C) Mercury in Cancer.
(D) Saturn in Fifth House, Sun in Eleventh House and Mars, Saturn, Uranus, Pluto, Moon's nodes (one or more in one Eighth House).
(E) Mars and Saturn in Tenth House, and Sun in First, Fourth, or Eighth House.
(F) Moon and Mars in Sixth or Eighth House and Ruler of the First House in Seventh House from the position of Moon and Mars.
(G) Saturn in First, Fourth, Seventh, or Tenth House and Ruler of the First House in Eighth House, Moon's North node in Sixth House brings diseases of nutritional deficiency at the age of 26.

DIARRHEA

Saturn or Moon's North node in Second House.

DYSENTERY

Mercury with Moon's North node in First House and Saturn and Mars in Seventh House.

DISEASE OF ASCITES

(A) Saturn in Cancer and Moon in Aries.
(B) Moon's North node in First House and Sun and Moon in Eleventh House bring sickness at the age of 19.

DISEASE OF THE SPLEEN

(A) When Moon is lord of First or Sixth or Seventh House and Mars in Sixth or Seventh or Tenth House, from the Moon. Saturn in Fourth, Seventh, or Eleventh House from the Moon or Uranus or Pluto or Moon's nodes in Seventh House from Moon.
(B) Moon and Saturn in Fifth House.
(C) Birth time at night (i.e., between sunset and sunrise in waning Moon fortnight) and Saturn in First or Fourth or Seventh House.

TUMOR

(A) Saturn in First House—and Moon in Eighth House

in weak sign—with Mars, Saturn, Uranus, Pluto, Moon's node.

(B) Ruler of the Sixth in Twelfth House and Ruler of the Twelfth House in Sixth House bring tumors at the age of 15 or 30.

SMALLPOX

Mars in First House and Sun in Seventh House from Mars and Saturn Fourth, Seventh, or Eleventh House.

WOMEN'S DISEASES

Mars and Venus in Seventh House.

HEMORRHOIDS (PILES)

(A) Saturn in Twelfth House, Ruler of the First House and Mars in Seventh House.

(B) Mars in Seventh House and Sun in First House.

(C) Saturn in Twelfth House and Mars in Sixth, Seventh, or Tenth House from Saturn or Uranus, Pluto, or Moon's nodes in Seventh House from Saturn.

(D) Mars with Ruler of the First House.

(E) Saturn in Twelfth House and Mars in Sixth, Seventh, or Tenth House from Saturn, or Ruler of the First House in Seventh House from Saturn.

(F) Mars in Seventh House from the ruler of the First House.

INFLAMMATION OF THE MOUTH

Venus or Jupiter ruler of Sixth House placed in First House and Mars in Sixth, Seventh, or Tenth House or Saturn in Fourth, Seventh, or Eleventh House or Uranus, or Pluto or Moon's node in Seventh House from First House.

DISEASE OF THE UMBILICAL REGION (CHILDREN)

Ruler of the Sixth in Third House.

SYPHILIS AND GONORRHEA

Jupiter in Twelfth House.

INCURABLE DISEASES

Sickness comes at the age of 17 if Jupiter, Mercury, and Venus are in Eighth House.

VARIOUS PAINS AND ACHES

(A) Ruler of the Eleventh House in Third House.
(B) Jupiter in Third House and Venus in sign Leo in First, Fourth, Fifth, Seventh, Ninth, Tenth House from the First House.
(C) Saturn, Mars in Sixth or Twelfth House.

ARTHRITIS

(A) Birth at night and Sun in Fifth House with Mars, Saturn, Uranus, Pluto, Moon's nodes (with one or more than one).
(B) Sun and Moon in Sixth or Twelfth House.

EPILEPSY

(A) Saturn, Mars in Sixth or Eighth House.
(B) Moon and Venus in First, Fourth, Seventh, or Tenth House and Mars, Saturn, Uranus, Pluto, Moon's node (more than one) in Eighth House from First House.
(C) Moon, Saturn together and Mars Sixth or Seventh or Tenth from them.
(D) Moon in Scorpio in Sixth, Eighth, or Twelfth House with Mars, Saturn, and Moon's North node.
(E) Saturn and Moon's North node in Eighth House and Mars, Uranus, Pluto in First, Fifth, or Ninth Houses of Horoscope.
(F) Sun and Mars in Sixth, Eighth, or Twelfth House.

SCHIZOPHRENIA

(A) Scorpio, Moon—in First, Fifth, or Ninth House with Mars, Saturn, Uranus, Pluto, Moon's nodes (with one or more than one).
(B) Scorpio, Moon with Mercury in First House.
(C) Mercury in Third, Sixth, Eighth, or Twelfth House with Mars, Saturn, Uranus, Pluto, Moon's nodes (with one or more than one).
(D) Jupiter in First House and Saturn or Mars in Seventh House.
(E) Saturn in First House and Mars in First, Fifth, Seventh, or Ninth House.

(F) Scorpio, Moon with Saturn in Twelfth House.
(G) Saturn in First House, Sun in Twelfth House, Mars or Moon in First, Fifth, or Ninth House.
(H) Saturn Ruler of the Second with Mars, Uranus, Pluto, Moon's nodes (with one or more than one).
(I) Ruler of Second House and Saturn with Sun or Mars.
(J) Cancer, Scorpio, or Pisces, ascendant and ruler of the Third House with Jupiter in First House.
(K) Sun or Ruler of the First House in First or Fourth House.

RINGWORM

Mercury, Sun, and Moon in Seventh House and other planets in Fourth House bring sickness at the age of 16.

CHRONIC ILLNESSES

(A) Mercury in Aries, Moon in Tenth House, and Saturn and Mars together in any other House.
(B) Moon, Mercury, and Ruler of the First House with Moon's North or South node.
(C) Mars in First House, Sun in Eighth House, and Saturn in Fourth House.
(D) Mercury, Jupiter, and Sun in Sixth or Eighth House, ruler of the First House Mars, Saturn, or Moon's nodes.
(E) Ruler of the First House Mercury or Mars with Moon and Moon's nodes.

GOITER

(A) Moon, Ruler of the First and Sixth House in Sixth, Eighth, or Twelfth House.
(B) Ruler of the First House with Sun in Sixth, Eighth, or Twelfth House.

ULCER

(A) Ruler of the First House with Mars in Sixth, Eighth, or Twelfth House.
(B) Saturn and Mars in Sixth or Twelfth House.
(C) Ruler of the First House and Mars in Sixth, Eighth, or Twelfth House.
(D) Ruler of the First and Eighth House in Sixth House with Saturn or Moon's nodes.
(E) Mars in Third, Sixth, or Eleventh House and Venus in Twelfth House.
(F) Moon in Twelfth House with Jupiter, Mercury in Sixth or Eleventh House.
(G) Mars in First House and Venus or Jupiter in Seventh House.
(H) Saturn in Eighth House and Mars in Seventh House.
(I) Ruler of the Sixth House in Fifth House with Mars, Saturn, Uranus, Pluto, Moon's nodes (one or more).

GLOSSARY

AFFLICTION—When a planet is adversely aspected by being square, semi-square, sesquare, or in opposition to one or more other planets, the condition is called an affliction. In medical astrology, an affliction sometimes also includes the conjunction and parallel with Mars, Saturn, Uranus, Neptune, and Pluto.

ANGLES—The angles of the horoscope are the four cardinal points; the mid-heaven (abbr. M.C.), the nadir (abbr. I.C.), the ascendant and the descendant. Ther correspond to the First, Fourth, Seventh, and Twelfth Houses.

ASCENDANT—The degree of the zodiac that is on the eastern horizon at the time of birth or at any other moment under consideration. The zodiacal sign occupying that position is called the *rising sign*.

ASPECT—An aspect is the relative position of two planets as determined by the number of degrees separating them. Good aspects are the trine (120 deg.) and the sextile (60 deg.). The evil or inharmonious aspects are the semi-square (45 deg.), the square (90 deg.), the sesquiquadrate (135 deg.), and the opposition (180 deg.).

BENEFICS—The planets Jupiter and Venus, and the Sun, are called benefics because their influences are benevolent.

CONJUNCTION—When two planets are within six degrees of each other, the aspect is called a conjunction.

CUSP—On a birth chart, the cusp is the line dividing two houses. The cusp of the First House is the ascendant;

that of the Fourth House, the nadir or imum coeli; that of the Tenth House, the mid-heaven or medium coeli.

DECANATE—Ten degrees, or one-third of a zodiacal sign.

DECUMBITURE—The exact time at which a person takes to his bed with an illness. Older physician-astrologers used that time to erect an horary figure by which they might determine the character, prognosis, and termination of a given illness. It was used also to ascertain critical days, based on the Moon's aspects.

DETRIMENT—When a planet occupies a sign which is directly opposite the zodiacal sign over which it has rulership, it is said to be in its detriment. Some authorities also include the sign opposite that of a planet's exaltation as being a detriment.

ECLIPTIC—The Sun's apparent path around the Earth, during which it passes among the constellations.

EXALTATION—The position of a planet in the zodiac from which it exerts a powerful influence. (See Appendix II.)

FALL—The position of a planet in the zodiac opposite that of its exaltation, and from which it exerts only a feeble influence. (See Appendix II.)

FIGURE—A horoscope, diagram, or scheme, representing the heavens at a given moment. It is also called a geniture, chart, map, and nativity.

HOUSE—The horoscope or natal chart is divided into twelve equal divisions of 30 deg. each. These segments are called *houses*. They are regarded as stationary in respect to the horizon.

NATIVITY—See *Figure*.

RADICAL—Pertaining to the so-called root of a nativity or the horoscope at birth.

RADIX—The horoscope at birth, or the state of the heavens at the moment of time taken for erecting a horary figure.

RETROGRADE PLANET—When, owing to the Earth's relative motion, a planet appears to move backward through the zodiac, it is said to be retrograde. Traditional astrologers consider retrogradation as a debility, but some modern practitioners argue against that theory, pointing out that a retrograde planet is actually drawing nearer to the Earth and, therefore, its influence should be increasing.

RISING SIGN—See *Ascendant*.

TESTIMONY—A term originally used by Ptolemy, meaning reasons offered in support of a judgment, and based upon a plant's influence or configuration. The word is synonymous with *argument*.

TRANSIT—The passage of a planet over the place or longitude of any other planet, Significator, or cusp of a house in a horoscope is called a *transit*.

TRINE—An aspect of 120 deg. It is considered the most perfect and harmonious of all aspects, since it forms an equilateral triangle, symbolical of a unified trinity.

ZODIAC—An imaginary belt extending around the heavens, marking the path of all the principal planets and Moon, and having as its central line the ecliptic or Sun's path. Some authorities hold it to be 14 deg. in width, and others 16 deg. or 18 deg. The zodiac is divided into twelve divisions, called Sun signs.

SELECTED BIBLIOGRAPHY

BARBAULT, ANDRE. *De la psychanalyse a l'astrologie.*

BENJAMINE, ELBERT. *Stellar Healing.* Los Angeles: Church of Light Books, 1947.

BLAGRAVE, JOSEPH. *Astrological Practice of Physic.* London: 1670.

BUTLER, H. E. *Solar Biology.* Applegate, Cal.: Esoteric Brotherhood, 1928.

CAREY, GEORGE WASHINGTON. *The Zodiac and the Salts of Salvation.* Los Angeles: 1929.

CARTER, CHARLES E. *An Encylopedia of Psychological Astrology.* London: 1924.

COLLIN, RODNEY. *The Theory of Celestial Influence.* London: Stuart and Watkins, 1968.

CORNELL, HOWARD. *Encyclopedia of Medical Astrology.* Los Angeles: 1936.

CULPEPPER, NICHOLAS. *Astrological Judgment of Diseases.* London: 1655. Washington, D.C.: National Astrological Library, 1959.

DAATH, HEINRICH. *Medical Astrology.*

DOANE, DORIS CHASE. *Astrology: 30 Years Research.* Los Angeles: Graphic Arts Press, 1956.

GAUQUELIN, MICHEL. *The Cosmic Clocks.* Chicago: Henry Regnery, 1967.

————. *The Scientific Basis of Astrology.* New York: Stein & Day, 1969.

HEINDEL, MAX. *Astro-Diagnosis.* Oceanside, Cal.: Rosicrucian Fellowship, 1929.

————. *Occult Principles of Health and Healing.* Oceanside, Cal.: Rosicrucian Fellowship, 1938.

————. *Simplified Scientific Astrology.* Oceanside, Cal.: Rosicrucian Fellowship, 1928.

LLEWELLYN, GEORGE. *How Planets Affect You.* Los Angeles: Church of Light, 1930.

MORRISH, FURZE. *Outline of Astro-Psychology.*

PEARCE, ALFRED JOHN. *Textbook of Astrology*. London: 1911.

RAPHAEL. *Medieval Astrology*. London: 1910.

SAUNDERS, RICHARD. *The Astrological Judgment and Practice of Physic*. London: 1677.

SAWTELL, VANDA. *Astrology and Biochemistry*. London: Health Science Press, 1947.

SIMMONITE, W. J. *Complete Arcana of Astral Philosophy*. London: 1897.

THIERENS, A. *Elements of Esoteric Astrology*. London: 1936.

TUCKER, WILLIAM J. *Astromedical Diagnosis*. Sidcup. (Kent) England: Pythagorean Publications, 1959.

————. *Astromedical Research*. Sidcup.: Pythagorean Publications, 1962.

————. *The Principles of Scientific Astrology*. New York: J. B. Lippincott, 1938.

TURNBULL, COULSON. *The Divine Language of Celestial Correspondence*. Orange, Cal.: 1926.

THE
EDGAR CAYCE
SERIES

These distinguished books on the life and work of America's most famous clairvoyant, EDGAR CAYCE, are all prepared under the supervision of his son, HUGH LYNN CAYCE, to insure authenticity.

EDGAR CAYCE ON JESUS AND HIS CHURCH
by Anne T. Read (65-975/95¢)
THE EDGAR CAYCE READER #2 (64-086/75¢)
edited by Hugh Lynn Cayce
EDGAR CAYCE ON HEALING (65-845/95¢)
by Mary Ellen Carter and William A. McGarey, M.D.
EDGAR CAYCE ON PROPHECY (64-777/75¢)
by Mary Ellen Carter
EDGAR CAYCE ON ATLANTIS (64-762/75¢)
by Edgar Evans Cayce
HIGH PLAY (66-738/$1.25)
by Harmon Hartzell Bro, Ph. D.
EDGAR CAYCE ON REINCARNATION (65-752/95¢)
by Noel Langley
STRANGER IN THE EARTH (65-456/95¢)
by Thomas Sugrue
EDGAR CAYCE ON THE DEAD SEA SCROLLS
by Glenn D. Kittler (65-494/95¢)
EDGAR CAYCE ON RELIGION AND PSYCHIC EXPERIENCE
by Harmon Hartzell Bro, Ph. D. (65-216/95¢)

ENJOY THESE GREAT
WARNER PAPERBACK LIBRARY
BESTSELLERS!